Produ
Foc

One of the most s
can economy dur
era has been the pervasive importance of innovation. The nature, sources, and effects of innovation are subjects of concern to virtually everyone, from the Congressional committee investigating technological change to the housewife reading the label on a new type of frozen vegetable in a supermarket.

This study deals with product innovation, and with some of the problems created by it, in the food processing industries. Innovation has become a major dimension of competition among the larger food processing companies, and thus an understanding of the nature and effects of new products seems essential in any attempt to explain or evaluate competition in food marketing.

The book begins with an attempt to answer the question: What is a new product? For the food processor there are three classes of new products: product improvements, product line extensions, and distinctly new products. From the distributor's viewpoint there are new items, new brands, and new types of products. The authors studied the extent of innovation in 21 product categories and the sources of new food products.

Because of the high costs of new product R&D and market introduction, large food proc-

Product Innovation in Food Processing
1954–1964

essors have become increasingly important as a source of new products. Sales of a new product after its introduction tend to follow one of three basic patterns: steady growth, growth and decline, or steady decline. Of the 127 distinctly new food products covered in this study, over 40% had failed to break even after two years of regular distribution.

The book ends with an appraisal of the effects of new products on food costs to consumers, on corporate growth and profits, on food distributors and their buying committees, and on the economy as a whole and price competition.

The authors are Robert D. Buzzell, Professor of Business Administration, Harvard Business School, and Robert E. M. Nourse, formerly Research Associate, now Assistant Professor of Business Administration, The University of Western Ontario.

PRODUCT INNOVATION IN FOOD PROCESSING
1954–1964

ROBERT D. BUZZELL
Professor of Business Administration
Harvard University

ROBERT E. M. NOURSE
Assistant Professor of Business Administration
The University of Western Ontario
Formerly Research Associate, Harvard University

Division of Research
Graduate School of Business Administration
Harvard University
Boston · 1967

Foreword

THIS STUDY began in the usual way in the spring of 1965 as a purely academic type project under the Division of Research. It subsequently benefited enormously by its being combined in large part with a broader study conducted by Arthur D. Little, Inc., (ADL) to provide information for the National Commission on Food Marketing, which had been established by President Johnson in July 1964. ADL had been commissioned by the Grocery Manufacturers of America, Inc., (GMA) to undertake a program of studies for submission to the Commission. In June 1965 Professor Buzzell was asked to participate in this study program, and when he had explained his interest in new product development, he was asked to follow out this interest in the food processing industry.

Through this connection with the GMA sponsored studies, the researchers were able to obtain superb cooperation from food processors in providing data from their own records and through them from the A. C. Nielson Company on sales trend data. The expenses involved in the processing of these data for analysis were also borne by the sponsored program. The design of the study itself, however, the data requests, and the analytical plan were developed entirely by the researchers; fortuitously these plans coincided with the needs of the sponsored research as well as the objectives of the original project developed here.

Of the material presented in this volume, the content of Chapters 4 and 5 appeared in a preliminary form in the ADL report submitted by the GMA to the Commission. Chapter 6 is derived from material which was developed for that report but did not appear as such in the report. The remaining material was developed for this project alone and was not a part of the sponsored research.

The focusing of this research relating to new product development into the food processing field supplements other work going forward at the School. The Division has just published two papers on brand strategy in food marketing in the United States and will soon publish a study of the problems of introducing new food products into supermarkets. Several other studies in the agribusiness research program either currently in press or nearing completion also cover other aspects of the food processing and marketing field. The findings of these studies are mutually reinforcing in providing empirical findings relating to innovations in food processing.

This volume also relates to another program of research just getting under way. This program involves studies of the dynamics of competition in American industry, and the ways in which a variety of competitive policies affect the behavior and performance of industries in relation to the public interest. The importance and contribution of new product innovation to competition in food processing is set forth clearly in this study and emphasizes the need to extend such studies into other industries.

May I express again for the School our gratitude to the Grocery Manufacturers of America and to Arthur D. Little for the financial support and cooperation that contributed so much to the richness of the findings of the study. The financial support of the researchers themselves as well as a portion of the out-of-pocket expenses came from an endowment in support of research provided by a donor who prefers to remain anonymous. Our thanks to this donor continue to mount.

BERTRAND FOX
Director of Research

May 1967

Preface

ONE OF THE MOST STRIKING features of the American economy during the post-World War II era has been the pervasive importance of innovation. The nature, sources, and effects of innovation are subjects of concern to virtually everyone, from the Congressional committee investigating technological change to the housewife reading the label on a new type of frozen vegetable in a supermarket.

There are many kinds of innovation, ranging from basic advances in scientific knowledge to the creation of new dance steps. From an economic standpoint, however, the most significant type of innovation is that associated with the development of new and improved products. Expenditures intended for new product development account for the bulk of the massive outlays made annually by American industry on research and development. The result of this large and growing level of effort has been a so-called "new product explosion" throughout the economy. This explosion, in turn, has created new problems for business executives, for consumers, and for government agencies involved in the regulation of business practice.

This study deals with product innovation, and with some of the problems created by it, in the food processing industries. Generally speaking, technological changes in food processing since 1945 have been less dramatic than those which have taken place in such "glamour" industries as electronics and chemicals. But many new food products have nevertheless been developed and introduced, and innovation has become a major dimension of competition among the larger food processing companies. Thus, an understanding of the nature and effects of new products seems essential in any attempt to explain or evaluate competition in food marketing.

This study was undertaken in an effort to clarify certain issues related to product innovation in the food processing industries, as explained in Chapter 1. The need for clarification of these issues became apparent as a result of earlier efforts by the authors to study some of the specific management problems associated with new product development and introduction. Initial discussions of these problems with marketing executives and marketing research personnel in several firms revealed an unfortunate lack of information and even of uniform terminology on the subject of new products. It was concluded that a basic empirical study was needed as a foundation for any investigation of particular management problems and practices.

By a fortunate coincidence, realization of the need for a broad study of new food products was followed shortly by an opportunity to obtain cooperation and financial support for it. In July 1964 President Johnson established a National Commission on Food Marketing to study recent changes in food markets and marketing practices. The staff of the Commission began its work in early 1965 and asked the major companies and trade associations in the field to cooperate by supplying various kinds of information. Some industry groups went beyond passive compliance with these requests and undertook studies on their own initiative. The Grocery Manufacturers of America retained Arthur D. Little, Inc., to coordinate a series of studies under the general supervision of Professors Jesse W. Markham of Princeton University and Charles C. Slater of Michigan State University. The authors of this book were asked to conduct one of the studies in this program, on the subject of new products. Because of the circumstances surrounding the study, we were able to secure unusually full cooperation from the participating companies in providing information of a highly confidential nature.

The authors are indebted to many persons for assistance and encouragement during the conduct of this study. First, we wish to thank the members of the Grocery Manufacturers of America committee which served to coordinate the association's research program, especially its chairman, Mr. Herbert M. Cleaves of the General Foods Corporation. Jesse Markham and Charles Slater, the technical directors of the GMA research program, made important contributions to the design of the study. In the survey of food processors on which most of our findings are based, we were ably assisted by Dr. Gary Marple and Miss Ellen Metcalf of Arthur D. Little, Inc. Mr. Harry Wissmann of Arthur D. Little handled most of the negotiations with the GMA committee and was responsible for obtaining its initial agreement to sponsor this study.

Once the study was approved, the burden of completing the survey questionnaires fell upon the marketing executives and marketing research personnel of the participating companies. We sincerely appreciate the efforts which they made on our behalf, as well as the helpful suggestions which they contributed. We regret that we cannot acknowledge these contributions by names without violating the conditions of confidentiality under which information was released to us.

Apart from the GMA-sponsored survey, our principal sources of information were the A. C. Nielsen Company and "Grand Valley Markets," a large food chain company. Mr. James O. Peckham, Executive Vice-President of A. C. Nielsen, was very cooperative and helpful in supplying data to us, under a special agreement with the companies for which it was originally collected. The Grand Valley Markets data would not have been saved, much less analyzed, except for the foresight and persuasive abilities of Mr. William Applebaum. We deeply appreciate Mr. Applebaum's help in obtaining these records for our use and his many valuable suggestions on the study as a whole. We are also indebted to the management of Grand Valley Markets for permitting us to use their data.

Finally, we wish to thank our colleagues at the Harvard Business School who reviewed earlier drafts of the study and made numerous contributions to it. In addition to Mr. Applebaum, Professor Theodore Levitt read the entire first draft and suggested many improvements. Professor Bertrand Fox, Director of Research, likewise helped us through the many problems of shaping the raw material into a final draft. Last in sequence but not in importance, Miss Ruth Norton of the Division of Research did her usual fine job of editing, which has been reflected in all of the Division's publications in recent years.

Despite the fact that so many persons have helped us, we remain responsible for any errors that may have survived into the final draft.

ROBERT D. BUZZELL

ROBERT E. M. NOURSE

Soldiers Field
Boston, Massachusetts
May 1967

Contents

List of Tables

List of Figures

CHAPTER 1

Introduction

ONE DAY in the fall of 1965 four persons came into contact with new food products in the course of their normal affairs:

- IN SKOKIE, ILLINOIS,

Mrs. Barbara Locke, a 34-year-old housewife, went to a supermarket near her home. This particular shopping trip was rather special, because it was her first visit to an American supermarket in nearly three years. With her husband and their two children, Barbara had been living in Italy.

As she walked through the store, Barbara felt that it was at once strange and very familiar. "It's great," she thought "to be back to a *big* store, where I can get everything in one place." She noticed quite a few products in the store which she didn't remember having seen before, and she stopped to look at several of these products as she passed up and down the aisles.

One of the new products was a breakfast cereal which contained pieces of "freeze-dried" fruit. Barbara wondered if the children would eat the cereal. The fruit, she thought, couldn't taste much like fresh fruit. She suspected that the cereal was more expensive than regular cereal and fresh fruit. She wasn't sure, though—just how much fruit do you use with a box of cereal, anyway?

Barbara Locke decided to try a box of the new cereal, and she also bought a package of dehydrated *au gratin* potatoes. In this case she was reasonably sure that the cost (45 cents for four servings) was more than it would have been if she had bought raw potatoes and made her own sauce. "Even so," she thought, "it's well worth it to save all that time and trouble." Barbara seldom made *au gratin* potatoes, even though everyone in the family liked them. One reason was that she didn't always have cheddar cheese on hand. Besides, it *did* take a lot of time to cut up the potatoes, and grate the cheese, and. . . .

• IN PHILADELPHIA,

Jason Merrill, Controller of the Omnibus Food Corporation, shifted uneasily in his chair. For over an hour, he had been listening to a presentation dealing with "Product 63–12," a new synthetic frozen fruit juice concentrate. The Brand Manager who had been assigned to the new product had gone through dozens of charts and tables, but Jason noted that there were nearly as many more yet to go. Not only were meetings of the New Products Committee becoming more frequent, Jason thought, but each one seemed to take longer than the last.

The proposal for Product 63–12 had first been discussed in early 1963. At that time the committee had approved an expenditure of $100,000 for product development and testing. Since then, the laboratory had developed a product with acceptable flavor and consistency; taste trials had been conducted with small groups of housewives; then the product was modified and tested again, and modified again.

Now the Brand Manager was asking the New Products Committee to approve his test marketing plan, which called for an expenditure of $500,000 during the next year. This budget would provide for equipment to produce enough of the new juice concentrate for sale in the test markets, as well as for advertising and promotion. If the product were successful in the test markets, Jason Merrill knew that there would be another request for a much larger appropriation to buy full-scale processing equipment and to promote the product on a national basis.

Sometimes Jason Merrill thought to himself that he had become a "gamblin' man" in spite of his strict Baptist upbringing. Every new product which the committee approved was, in effect, a bet; and the odds against winning were rather high. Omnibus Foods was betting that consumers would accept the product; that competitors would not pre-empt the market by introducing similar products; that the cost estimates could be met; and so forth.

"Of course," Jason thought, "there really isn't any choice." Omnibus Foods was firmly committed to a policy of new product development. Only the week before, Elliott Brady, the president of Omnibus, had told a group of security analysts that over half of the company's sales in 1964 had come from products introduced since 1954.

Just then the Brand Manager started to review his sales and profit forecasts for Product 63–12. Jason Merrill couldn't help reflecting that if the sales forecasts for *all* of the company's new products had been achieved, total sales in 1964 would have been twice as great as they actually were. . . .

- IN LOS ANGELES,

Carl Zimmerman, a grocery buyer for Orange Blossom Markets, Inc., quickly finished reading an inventory report and hurried upstairs to the conference room. He was late for the weekly meeting for the Buying Committee and he knew that the agendum for the meeting was a full one. During the preceding week, Carl had listened to more than 30 presentations by salesmen who wanted Orange Blossom Markets to handle additional products. Not all of these were really "new," of course; some were just additional brands of such well-established products as canned applesauce and olives. But the weekly harvest did include several products which were being introduced to Orange Blossom's market area for the first time.

One of the products which Carl had heard about during the week was a semimoist dog food which contained meat but was not canned and did not require refrigeration; another was a new brand of powdered, nondairy coffee creamer; and a third was a refrigerated prebaked pie crust shell.

Carl had asked the salesmen who called upon him to complete a "New Product Description" form for each of the products which they wanted him to consider. These forms covered such basic information as suggested retail price, cost to Orange Blossom, advertising support provided by the manufacturer, and discounts and allowances available to Orange Blossom. The company had adopted the standardized information form during the mid-1950's, when the number of new product presentations had reached a point which made it difficult to evaluate each product systematically.

Carl estimated that, among them, he and the two other grocery buyers at Orange Blossom probably were exposed to over 3,000 new products each year. Only about a third of these products were discussed by the Buying Committee; the rest were eliminated by the buyers in their preliminary screening. Thus, on the average, the Buying Committee dealt with about 20 proposed additions to the product line per week; less than half of these were approved for trial in the stores, and many of those that were tried out didn't last very long.

For this week's meeting, Carl had nine new products to bring before the committee. He knew that the other members would expect him to be able to answer some difficult questions: Did Orange Blossom need a *third* brand of powdered coffee creamer? What was different about this one? The new dog food was a little lower-priced than the brand which the stores had been carrying, but was it as good? Was there any demand for a prebaked pie crust? Would breakage losses on such a fragile product offset its relatively high gross profit? These questions had to be asked because the company had to be careful not to adopt any new product which couldn't pay its own way. Each year the number of items listed in the Orange Blossom warehouse catalog went up, although the amount of shelf space in the stores remained almost constant. Carl wondered how long they could keep this up. . . .

• IN WASHINGTON D.C.,
   Bruce Wayne stared reflectively at a blank sheet of paper. Bruce, who was on leave from his position in the Economics Department of a well-known eastern university, was vainly trying to start writing the first draft of a report which was due in final form in 90 days. For the preceding six months Bruce had been reviewing an extensive collection of facts and figures dealing with the past and present operations of several food processing industries. As a member of the technical staff of the President's National Commission on Food Marketing, Bruce was responsible for drafting a report on the market structure, marketing behavior, and economic performance of the industries assigned to him.

   Bruce wanted to do the best job he could because he knew that his report, along with other technical studies, would be used by the Commission itself in preparing its overall report on food marketing; their conclusions, in turn, might have a substantial effect on future legislation regulating marketing practices. He found it hard to decide on the right approach to his report because the economic theory with which he was familiar did not seem to provide an adequate framework for analysis.

   For instance, there was the question of "concentration." Several of the food processing industries which Bruce was studying had become more concentrated since 1947; the share of total industry sales accounted for by the four largest firms was as high as 90% in one case. According to widely accepted ideas, such high levels of concentration were undesirable. On the other hand, Bruce knew that the larger food processing companies could claim credit for many of the new products which had been introduced during the past 20 years. Could the benefits of innovation be retained without the potential dangers of concentration?

   For that matter, just what *were* the benefits of innovation? Economic theory gave Bruce very little guidance here. The theory was based on an essentially static productive system; it dealt with the allocation of resources among a *given* set of products and services. If a new product was introduced into such a system, at a higher price than existing products of the same general type, were consumers better off?

Many of the new food products which Bruce had seen and heard about seemed frivolous to him, and he suspected that the only demand for such products was a purely artificial one created by heavy advertising and promotional expenditures. Orthodox economic theory suggested that such promotional costs represented economic waste, except for purely informational promotion. Was advertising for a "new, improved" breakfast cereal truly informational? Were the innovations and improvements real or imaginary? Bruce Wayne wondered where to begin. . . .

Benefits and Costs of New Products

The four individuals described in these episodes are, of course, fictitious. They are intended to be representative of the viewpoints of the four groups most directly concerned with, and affected by, new food products: consumers, food processors, food distributors, and government. The four episodes, equally fictitious, are designed to illustrate some of the potential benefits and costs of new food products for each of the four groups.[1] The importance of product innovation in the food processing industries is a direct function of these potential benefits and costs.

Consumer Benefits and Costs

For consumers like Barbara Locke and her family, the most important potential benefits of new food products are *increased choice, reductions in preparation and purchasing time, improvements in flavors,* and *improvements in nutrition.* Thus, for example, the availability of a new cereal containing freeze-dried fruit represents an additional choice, unless it is offset by a corresponding elimination of some older product. In most cases, there are *not* any offsetting reductions in assortments, as evidenced by the steady increases in the number of items carried by the typical American food store during the 1950's and 1960's. Both the cereal-cum-fruit and the dehydrated potatoes purchased by Bar-

---

[1] The word "cost" is used here in a broad sense and is meant to encompass all of the real or potential disadvantages of new products, financial and non-financial.

bara—especially the latter—permit reductions in preparation time. They are examples of the many convenience foods which have been developed since the late 1940's. Many of these convenience foods, and some other new food products, also benefit consumers in terms of reductions in the time required for purchasing. A housewife equipped with sufficient refrigerator and freezer space can now buy virtually all her family's needs for a week or more in a single shopping trip. Many new processed foods incorporate improvements in flavor, based on changes in processing methods, better packaging, and the use of new types of flavoring agents. Finally, some new products provide benefits in *nutrition*, either for consumers in general or for specific groups such as infants, elderly persons, or those concerned with overweight problems.

Barbara Locke's reactions to the two new products also illustrate some of the types of costs which may be associated with new products. In the first place, she estimates (with varying degrees of uncertainty) that both new items *cost more* (in direct monetary terms) than the conventional products or combinations of ingredients for which they are more or less direct substitutes. For most convenience foods her suspicion is likely to be confirmed, although many of the newer, highly processed products are actually less expensive than their conventional counterparts. (This point is discussed further in Chapter 6.) Either way, she finds it difficult to make meaningful price comparisons. Moreover, the benefits of variety carry with them the inherent problem of *confusion*, arising from greater and more diverse product assortments. On this point, the Consumer Advisory Council commented in its report to President Johnson, submitted in mid-1966, that ". . . the increasing breadth of choice makes it difficult for the consumer to be well informed." [2]

In appraising particular new products consumers like Barbara Locke must usually balance benefits against costs, possible advantages against risks. Neither the benefits nor the costs are likely to be of great consequence in any one transaction. The *most* that Barbara Locke can lose by trying the new breakfast cereal is its purchase price, perhaps 49 cents, and whatever irritation and loss

---

[2] Quoted in *Advertising Age*, June 27, 1966, p. 8.

of esteem may be associated with its rejection by her children. The maximum potential gain is likewise inconsequential, at least for the vast majority of American households. The effects of many millions of such transactions during the course of a year are not inconsequential, however, and for this reason product innovation in food processing may have a significant impact on consumer welfare.

Benefits and Costs for Processors and Distributors

For food processing companies like Omnibus Food Corporation, the principal attraction of new products is the expectation of increased sales and profits. It is generally accepted that continued growth in either sales or profits becomes progressively more difficult—perhaps impossible—as a product becomes older (see Chapter 6). This, in turn, implies that a company's total sales and profits are likely to stabilize, and eventually to decline, unless it can inject new blood into its product line from time to time. For this reason, most large food processors have adopted formal policies with regard to product innovation, and they are spending increasing amounts of money and effort on research and development programs and on marketing research related to new products.

The problems of product innovation are much more serious, or at least more directly related to individual decisions, for food processors than for consumers. As Jason Merrill noted, the costs of developing and introducing even a single product are usually substantial; coupled with this is the risk of new product failure with an attendant inability to recoup any of the money spent on development and introduction. Partly because of the costs and risks involved, new product planning and control has also become a complex and time-consuming activity in most food processing companies. New forms of organization, such as the committee which absorbed so much of Jason Merrill's time, have evolved. New research techniques, and refinements of old ones, have been developed to evaluate new products at various stages in their development.

The "assets and liabilities" of new products for distributors are generally similar to those for processors, except that the distributors' potential gains or losses associated with any single product are much smaller. Thus, the main benefit of new products for Orange Blossom Markets is that of *maintaining or increasing* sales and profits. The episode of Carl Zimmerman illustrates some of the associated problems: like the processing companies, food chains and wholesalers have had to develop *new organizational* arrangements—such as buying committees—to cope with the problems of evaluating new products. They have also developed more systematic procedures *for obtaining and evaluating relevant information*, and some chains have even created facilities and methods for sales testing new products within their stores.

Government Agencies

In the United States various agencies, within both the executive and the legislative branches of the Federal Government, are concerned with new food products. The Department of Agriculture conducts an extensive research program aimed at the development and testing of new products, and some of the products introduced during the post-World War II period have been based at least in part on the results of this research. Other agencies, including the Federal Trade Commission, the Department of Justice, and special bodies such as the National Commission on Food Marketing and the Consumer Advisory Council, are concerned with the measurable economic effects of product innovation. Presumably, the appropriate viewpoint for these agencies is that of the economy *as a whole*; hence, Bruce Wayne was interested in new products as an aspect of economic performance in food processing, and as a factor which might affect other performance objectives.

For the economy as a whole, the most important benefits of new products are presumed to be higher consumer living standards and (possibly) opportunities for the entry of new competitors in an industry. "Higher living standards" embraces all the consumer benefits discussed above. Indeed, in the long run there is no real difference between the interests of "the consumer" and those of "the economy." An economist, however, is likely to place somewhat greater emphasis on the indirect effects of innovation, such as economic growth (which presumably creates higher levels of income and employment) and the maintenance of competition (which is thought to protect the consumer from exploitation).

The most apparent cost of new food products, from a broad economic viewpoint, is the expenditure of resources on product development and introduction, much of which is "wasted" on unsuccessful products. According to some economists, the growing emphasis on new products may also contribute to higher levels of concentration in industry. Most product research and development is conducted by *large* food processors. Insofar as this implies a tendency for the big to get bigger, it is regarded by some observers as a factor encouraging concentration.

Some Basic Issues

Despite the importance of new food products, very little information is available about product innovation in food processing industries. This is not to say that the subject has been ignored. Indeed, so much has been written about new products during the 1950's and 1960's that even a representative bibliography would fill many pages. Moreover, virtually every trade association meeting in the food processing and distributing industries includes one or more speeches on the management problems of new products. In all this literature, however, there is little factual information about the nature, extent, and effects of product innovation. Few subjects have been so much discussed on such a small base of reliable information. To cite just one example, the assertion that "80% of new products are failures" has been repeated many times, not just in speeches by food industry executives, but even in scholarly journals. (This same figure has also been widely applied to other industries, and to manufacturing industry in general.) The best that can be said about this estimate is that it is meaningless, because its terms are not defined. What is a "new product"? Which ones are included in the base of 100% against which the failure rate is computed; just products actually introduced to the market? All products to which R&D effort has been devoted? What constitutes failure? These are some of the questions that must be answered in arriving at a meaningful estimate of the "failure rate" for new products in an industry, or for all industries. The failure rate is but one of a series of issues related to product innovation which are subject to uncertainty and controversy, partly because of the lack of basic information on the nature, extent, costs, profits, and other effects of new product development and introduction.

The issues with which this study deals can conveniently be stated as questions:

What is a new product? One of the most basic issues related to new products is that of definition. The phrase "new product" has been used with a variety of meanings, and this has contributed to the confusion surrounding such other issues as that of the new product failure rate. Without an unambiguous definition of a new product, it is not possible to measure, analyze, or evaluate product innovation activities at all.

A *set* of definitions of the phrase "new product" is offered in Chapter 2. As explained there, it is not possible to use a single definition for all purposes.

How many new food products have been introduced during the post-World War II period or specific time intervals within that period? How important are new food products in terms of sales volume? In view of the diversity of terminology discussed above, it is hardly surprising that estimates of the extent of product innovation in food processing industries range from "a great deal" to "not very much." Secretary of Agriculture Orville Freeman was recently quoted as saying that: "Each year about 5,000 new food products are offered to stores that already carry some 8,000 different items."[3] A very different picture is implied by a report presented to Grocery Manufacturers of America by A. C. Nielsen Company in November 1965: ". . . 95% of today's (1965) volume of manufacturers' advertised brands (in 71 classes of products sold by food stores) comes from brands that were already on the market in 1961." [4]

These two statements are not directly comparable, of course, but even with due allowance for differences in definition, they seem contradictory. For a variety of purposes, it would be useful to know what the rate of new product introduction has been during a given period. For example, in evaluating the economic performance of,

---

[3] Quoted in *This Week,* June 26, 1966, p. 2.
[4] "Manufacturers' Advertised Brands: The Consumer's Choice," presentation to 57th Annual Meeting, Grocery Manufacturers of America, Inc., New York, November 9, 1965 (Chicago, A. C. Nielsen Company, 1966), p. 14.

say, the breakfast cereal industry, it might be relevant to compare the number of new products introduced in one period with the corresponding number for an earlier period. Is it really true that the *rate* of innovation is increasing? There is no way to know without first establishing unequivocal definitions and then collecting data based on those definitions. As far as the authors are aware, no reliable figures of this kind are available for any major industry.

What steps are involved in product development, testing, and introduction, and what are the costs of carrying out these steps? A bookshelf could easily be filled with literature on the subject of what, in the writers' opinions, *should* be done in the process of carrying a product from the idea stage through its full-scale introduction into the marketplace. Very little information has been available, however, on what actually is done, or how much it costs.

Empirical information of this kind might be useful for a variety of purposes. For example, during the early 1960's several companies in food processing and other industries were experimenting with the use of network analysis methods (such as the Critical Path Method and PERT) for planning and controlling new product development activities.

The use of these methods requires that estimates be made of the *time requirements* and the probable costs of the various steps involved in developing a product, testing it, designing packages, etc. The usefulness of network analysis methods depends on the accuracy of these time and cost estimates, among other things. How should the estimates be made? Some companies have compiled systematic records of their own past activities, but even this kind of internal "research" is the exception rather than the rule. Even for companies that have studied their own histories, it would be helpful to have representative figures for the time and cost requirements of new product development and introduction in other similar companies. The only information of this sort available in published form is for isolated cases or examples; no meaningful averages or other standards for comparison with a company's own performance have been developed. It seems likely that empirical information of this kind would be useful to managers in food processing and distributing companies in various ways.

What is the typical pattern of growth for a new food prod-

uct? The concept of the product life cycle has been widely discussed and is accepted by many marketing practitioners, as well as by most academic researchers, as a valid general model of sales trends for new products. In most of the articles and speeches dealing with the product life cycle, however, there is a basic ambiguity: does the model apply to product *classes or types* (such as instant coffee) or to individual brands (such as Instant Maxwell House), or to both? If there are common patterns in sales trends for individual new products, a knowledge of these patterns would be very useful to food processors in making sales forecasts and in preparing budgets based on these forecasts.

What proportion of all the new food products introduced are "successful"? A standard introductory gambit in most discussions of new products, either in general or in a given industry, is to view with alarm the high rate of new product failure. As mentioned earlier, it is frequently asserted that 80% or even 90% of all new products are failures. Any estimate of the actual rate of new product failure depends, obviously, on the definition of new product which is used. Such an estimate also depends on what criteria are used to classify products as successes and failures. A product which is regarded as a success by one company may be viewed as a dismal flop by another company; even within a given firm a product which meets one standard may fail by another. For this reason, the development of useful information about new product performance will require some more refined classification than a simple dichotomy of success and failure. Factual information about the performance of new food products, based on explicit measures of performance, would be useful to management in food processing companies for comparison with individual company results. Representative measures of new product performance would also be useful to economists as one aspect of the over-all economic performance of a given industry.

Objectives and Methods

The broad purpose of this study was to provide some factual information about new products in one important segment of the American economy—the food processing industries. It is hoped that the results of the study will contribute to a partial clarification of some of the issues discussed in the preceding section. Although the scope of the study is too limited to resolve all the questions related to product innovation in food processing, the results may nevertheless be useful to food processors and distributors and to others concerned with new food products.

Research Objectives

The specific objectives of this study were as follows:

1. *To develop a meaningful vocabulary for classifying new food products.* As indicated above, definitions are needed as a basis for compiling any kind of statistical information about new products. The definitions used in this study are stated and explained in Chapter 2.

2. *To provide a historical account of new food products introduced since World War II.* This historical account, which is given in Chapter 3, serves as a basis for estimating the number and sales importance of various types of new products and for determining the *sources* of product innovation. Limitations in the information available for analysis dictated that the statistical portion of the historical account be restricted, first, to selected product categories within the total universe of processed foods and, second, to the period 1954–1964.

3. *To describe the practices of major food processing companies in the development and introduction of new products.* This description, presented in Chapters 4 and 5, includes information about the *time spent* in new product research, development, testing, and introduction; the *costs incurred* for each of the activities involved; and the *results* of the activities.

4. *To ascertain whether there are any common patterns of sales growth and decline for new products following introduction.* As explained in Chapter 5, sales forecasting is an extremely important and difficult problem in the evaluation of a proposed new product. If there were common patterns in sales growth and decline, then a generalized model might be developed for forecasting purposes.

5. *To estimate the proportion of new food products which have been successful by various standards.* Three different criteria of success are discussed in Chapter 5, and estimates of the rate of success and failure based on each of these criteria are presented.

6. *To investigate some of the effects of new food products on consumers, processors, distributors, and the economy as a whole.* The discussion of effects, in Chapter 6, deals with the impact of product innovation on product variety and food costs from the consumer viewpoint; on the contribution of new products to processors' sales growth and profits; on the growing workload imposed on distributors by new products and their effects on distributors' gross margins; and it considers the influence of new products on economic concentration and the level of marketing costs. The evidence available is insufficient to permit definitive conclusions regarding any of these effects, but the issues involved are so important that even partial evaluation may be helpful.

Research Methods and Sources

This study is based primarily on two sources of information: a survey of food processors' new product development and introduction activities, and an analysis of the warehouse shipments data of a large food chain for the period 1954–1964. In addition, data obtained from the A. C. Nielsen Company were employed to estimate trends in sales of product categories on a national basis, and published sources of information were used to develop the historical background.

The survey of food processors was sponsored by the Grocery Manufacturers of America as part of a broad program of research coordinated by Arthur D. Little, Inc., and directed by Professors Jesse W. Markham of Princeton University and Charles C. Slater of Michigan State University. This research program was intended to provide information to the National Commission on Food Marketing, established by President Johnson in July 1964, to investigate and appraise recent changes in food markets and marketing practices.[5]

Food Processor Survey

The survey of food processors was carried out during the fall and winter of 1965. It included personal interviews, telephone inter-

---

[5] The Commission was established by Public Law 88–354, which was signed by the President on July 3, 1964. Its final report was submitted on July 1, 1966.

period were minimized. In total, more than 3,600 shipment entries were classified and analyzed.

Within each product category, and for each of the years studied, the percentage of sales accounted for by new *items, brands,*
and *types* of product was determined (definitions of these terms
are given in Chapter 2). A product was considered new if it had
not been stocked by the chain in the preceding even-numbered
year. For the year 1964 summary statistics were also derived to
show the percentage of sales accounted for by all new items,
brands, and types of product introduced in the full 10-year interval
since 1954. Finally, for each product category an *index of sales
volume* was computed for each period, using the 1954 period as a
base year with an index value of 100. Because the number of stores
operated by the retail chain had grown very rapidly between 1954
and 1964, however, the sales volume index was also adjusted to approximate more closely the average growth rate of all United
States food stores during this time period.

Because the warehouse shipments data summarized in Chapter 3
represent the experience of a single food chain, a question may be
raised about the extent to which they are representative of the entire United States market. A partial test of this question was made
by comparing Grand Valley Markets' warehouse catalogs with
those of three other large chains, each operating in a different re-
gion of the country (the other three chains did not have records of
warehouse *shipments* for earlier years; the old warehouse *catalogs*
simply listed the items stocked). This comparison indicated that
the numbers of new items, brands, and product types added by
Grand Valley were reasonably similar to the corresponding numbers for the other three chains, with one major exception. During
the period in question, Grand Valley expanded the number of private label products carried in various product categories more rapidly than the other chains. As a result, the figures given in Chapter 3 for "new brands" are undoubtedly somewhat higher than the
corresponding figures for the entire national market.

Product Categories Covered by the Study

At the outset of the GMA study, it was recognized that it would
not be possible to investigate *all* of the numerous industries en-

views, and a set of mailed questionnaire schedules. First, pilot interviews were conducted at several companies to determine what
kinds of information could be obtained and to establish a standardized vocabulary for use in large-scale data collection. On the
basis of these interviews and subsequent correspondence, data
schedules were developed for a mail survey. These schedules are
reproduced in the Appendix.

In the mail survey, schedules were sent to all the "major" companies in each product category selected for analysis and to a randomly selected sample of small firms. Major companies included
the manufacturers of all brands that held significant shares of the
total national market for a product category. In most cases, three
or four companies accounted for a susbtantial proportion of the total market and were classified as major processors.

There was considerable duplication among the major processors
in various product categories. As a result, the unduplicated list of
such firms for the 22 product categories covered included only 34
different companies. These companies were contacted by telephone and by mail in August 1965 to request cooperation in the
study. Because of the lack of relevant records and the unusually
confidential nature of the information requested, 10 of the 34
firms were unable and/or unwilling to participate in the survey. As
a result, 3 of the 22 product categories listed in the survey questionnaire (Schedule A, page 176, Appendix) were dropped. With
one or two exceptions, the 24 participating large firms accounted
for 50% or more of total national sales in each of the remaining
19 product categories.

Survey schedules were also mailed to 400 small processing firms,
selected randomly from those listed in *Thomas's Wholesale Grocery and Kindred Trades Register*.[6] Fewer than 20 completed schedules were returned by these small firms. Subsequent inquiries by
telephone and by mail revealed that very few of the small companies had engaged in new product development activities of the
kinds described in the questionnaires (see Schedules B and C, Appendix). As a result, the survey results summarized in Chapters 4
and 5 are confined to those provided by 24 large processing firms.

---

[6] 66th edition (New York, Thomas Publishing Company, 1964).

Each of these companies, with two exceptions, had total domestic sales of food products of $100 million or more in 1964.

The participating companies supplied information by mail at various points between August and December 1965. During this period each company was contacted by telephone at least once a month in order to clarify questions of definition and classification and to obtain supplementary information. In addition, the authors visited several of the companies to assist in completion of the schedules. All this effort was necessary because few of the companies had kept any systematic records of their past and present new product activities. Hence, the data requested in the survey had to be "reconstructed" from files and accounting records, and by interviews with personnel who were involved.

The information obtained from the processing firms is shown in the survey schedules, which are reproduced in the Appendix. Schedule A called for information about total company domestic sales of food products and total expenditures for marketing, marketing research, and product research and development on an annual basis for the period 1954–1964. Partially or entirely completed A schedules were received from 22 firms with aggregate 1964 food product sales of $6.98 billion. As shown in Chapters 3 and 6, analysis of trends in R&D expenditures and in marketing costs are based on slightly smaller numbers of companies.

Schedule B of the questionnaire provided the format for a standardized history of each *distinctly new product* introduced by the participating companies between 1954 and 1964. (The term "distinctly new product" is defined in Chapter 2.) Altogether, 19 companies provided such histories for 127 products.

Schedule C requested information about the companies' activities in the development and introduction of *product improvements* and *product line extensions* (for definitions, see Chapter 2). Although 20 companies supplied information on this subject, the data were inadequate for meaningful analysis and are not presented in this report.

Sales, Prices, and Advertising Expenditures

In addition to supplying data for individual new products, the cooperating food processors provided background information on sales, prices, and advertising expenditures in 17 of the 19 product

categories covered by the study. Estimates of *total retail sales, average retail prices,* and *total advertising expenditures* were obtained for each category, and for some other product categories, from A. C. Nielsen Company. The time periods covered by these data vary—in most cases, annual figures were obtained for years commencing about 1947 and running through 1964. These figures were used primarily to test certain hypotheses regarding product life cycles for food products. The conclusions of this part of the study have been reported in a separate publication.[7] The Nielsen data have also been used in the preparation of the histories of product innovation in each category which appear in Chapter 3.

The Nielsen estimates of retail sales of food products are based on store audits conducted in a national sample of food stores. Like all sample estimates, these figures are subject to error; but they are generally regarded in the food industries as the best available estimates of sales at the retail level.

"Grand Valley Markets" Warehouse Withdrawal Figures

A third major source of information for this study was a collection of warehouse withdrawal records during the period 1954–1964 for a major retail food chain. Thanks to the foresight of Mr. William Applebaum of the Harvard Business School, this company had preserved the tabulations of shipments of individual items from warehouses to stores for 4-week accounting periods since the early 1950's. Only a few of the older reports were missing, so the data provided an almost continuous record of products added and discontinued over an 11-year period. These data provide the primary basis for estimates of the *extent* of new product adoption in each category, given in Chapter 3.

Warehouse withdrawal records for Grand Valley Markets were analyzed for each of the *even-numbered* years 1954–1964 inclusive. Because of the enormous quantity of data involved in a full year of warehouse shipments, the analysis was restricted to four consecutive 4-week accounting periods, July–October, in each of the years under consideration. By utilizing four *consecutive* periods, the effects of fluctuations in shipments which occur in any *single* 4-week

7 Robert D. Buzzell, "Competitive Behavior and Product Life Cycles," in *New Ideas for Successful Marketing,* Proceedings of the 1966 World Congress, American Marketing Association, Chicago, 1966, pp. 46–68.

TABLE 1-1

Processed Food Product Categories Covered by This Study

	Covered in	
Product Category	Processor Survey	Chain Warehouse Shipments Analysis
Breakfast Cereals—Cold	X	X
Breakfast Cereals—Hot	X	X
Cake Mixes	X	X
Canned Vegetables	X	
Dehydrated Potatoes	X	X
Evaporated and Condensed Milk	X	X
Flour—All-Purpose	X	X
Frozen Dinners and Specialties	X	X
Frozen Juice Concentrates	X	X
Frozen Vegetables	X	X
Liquid Dietary Foods		X
Margarine	X	X
Nonfat Dry Milk		X
Packaged Dessert Mixes	X	X
Packaged Rice Products	X	X
Peanut Butter	X	X
Pet Foods	X	X
Powdered Coffee Creamers	X	X
Salad Dressings—Nonpourable	X	X
Salad Dressings—Pourable and Dry	X	X
Soluble (Instant) Coffee		X
Vegetable Shortening and Cooking Oil	X	X
Miscellaneous *	X	

* A very limited number of replies to the processor survey were also received
covering products in three categories: biscuits, cookies, and crackers; processed
cheese; and refrigerated dough products.

gaged in food processing. Accordingly, the study was restricted to a
group of major branches of food processing. These were selected so
as to include product categories in which the estimated rates of
new product introduction during the 1950's and 1960's had been
high, moderate, and low. The product categories selected on this
basis are listed in the first column of Table 1-1. In each of these cat-

egories, an attempt was made to obtain the types of information shown in Schedules B and C, reproduced in the Appendix, for *all* new products introduced between 1954 and 1964. Literally complete coverage was not possible in every product category, of course. The extent of *actual* coverage is indicated in the appropriate sections of Chapters 4 and 5.

Analysis of the food chain's warehouse shipments data was not begun until after the completion of the GMA-sponsored survey. The same product categories were selected for this second phase of the study, with one exception as shown in the second column of Table 1-1. Canned vegetables were excluded because of the extremely large number of varieties and brands handled by the chain over the 11-year period—many of them packers' labels which were not marketed on a regular, continuous basis.

Three product categories were included in the analysis of chain warehouse data which were *not* covered by the GMA survey: dry milk, soluble coffee, and liquid dietary foods.

Limitations of the Study

One important limitation has already been indicated: the study covers only selected product categories, not *all* processed foods. The selected categories, however, represented approximately 40% of all retail food sales in 1964 (exclusive of fresh meat, produce, dairy, and baked goods), so the results are believed to be broadly representative of the food processing industries.

Within the product categories studied there were some limitations in data arising from the scarcity of records and fallibility of memory for the earlier parts of the postwar period. For example, Nielsen data were not available (in most cases) for the first two or three years following the initial development of a product category. Similarly, the processing companies were unable to locate data for some individual products which were introduced in the earlier years of the study period. In several of the categories major processing companies were unable or unwilling to cooperate in the study at all. As a result, there are various gaps in the data. These are not believed to be so serious, however, as to distort the overall results significantly.

CHAPTER 2

What Is a "New Product"?

THERE IS considerable confusion over the meaning of the term "new product," not only as it applies to food products but also more generally. Even a cursory examination of recent speeches, articles, and books dealing with new products reveals a troublesome lack of uniformity in usage. At one extreme, some writers use the phrase "new product" to include not only *all* products which differ in any way from those previously produced or sold by a given company, but even changes in advertising appeals for existing products. Wasson, for example, says that: ". . . what is new depends on what the customer perceives, or can be brought to perceive. . . . Even the well established [product] can be 'new' so far as the buyer is concerned." [1]

At the other extreme, some commentators would exclude from the definition of new products everything except really fundamental innovations. Representative of this viewpoint is the statement by E. B. Weiss that: ". . . at least 80% of new products aren't new products at all. They are simply modifications—and minor modifications at that—of existing products." [2]

Despite disparities in current usage of the term, an unequivocal definition of a new product is an obvious prerequisite to intelligent discussion of the issues examined in this study. In Chapter 1, for example, we have suggested the need for estimates of the *number* of new products introduced in a given period, the *costs* involved in their development and introduction, and the relative *profitability* of new products at various points in time. Such estimates

[1] Chester R. Wasson, "What Is 'New' About a New Product?" *Journal of Marketing*, July 1960, pp. 52–56.
[2] E. B. Weiss, "That Malarky About 80% of New Products Failing," *Advertising Age*, August 2, 1965, p. 101.

cannot be made except on the basis of clear-cut definitions. Definition of a new product is therefore essential as a basis for compilation of statistical data and for any analysis based on these data.

This chapter deals with the various issues and problems associated with defining new products, and presents definitions on which later sections of the study are based.

Problems Associated with New Product Definition

The problems associated with definition of a new product apparently arise because both words, "new" and "product," are subject to varying interpretation. A product, on one hand, may mean a specific brand, flavor, or package size, such as a 3-ounce package of Jell-O strawberry-flavored gelatin. At the other extreme, product might equally well mean a broad group of foods used for similar purposes and/or occasions, such as breakfast foods, ranging from bacon to pancake mix to frozen Danish pastry. Many other interpretations falling between these two extremes are also possible. Product may refer to a general class of goods such as frozen foods; a category such as ready-to-eat breakfast cereals; or even a meaningful subcategory such as presweetened ready-to-eat breakfast cereals.

The word new is perhaps subject to even greater variation in meaning. To classify a product as new or not new requires consideration of such questions as the following:

1. *New to Whom?* Presumably, there are some consumers who have never used Jell-O and even some who have never heard of it before. Jell-O is new to these persons, although it has been on the market since the late 19th century. At the same time, recent editions of *Scripps-Howard Survey of Grocery Product Distribution* reveal that a small proportion of retail food stores do not stock Jell-O. If, in the future, one of these retailers should decide to start stocking the product, it would represent a new addition to the selection of goods offered by that store. Similarly, there are at this time a relatively small number of manufacturers engaged in producing and marketing gelatin desserts. If a processor not now doing so decided to market a gelatin dessert, it would be necessary for him to develop, test, and secure distribution for his product. The product would be considered new by the processor just entering the

field even though it might be substantially identical in form and content to the existing Jell-O.

2. *New in What Ways?* Changes in the basic composition of a product represent one way in which it can be new. Soft margarines are different in form and texture from regular margarines. Because they are soft, these margarines also require different packaging materials. Other new foods may utilize new ingredients, such as General Foods' Awake, a frozen orange juice concentrate utilizing synthetic flavorings in lieu of fresh oranges. New composition for a product may also necessitate new processing techniques. In introducing its Swedish Kreme biscuit, for example, United Biscuit Company employed a manufacturing process hitherto not used in the industry, in an attempt to approximate more closely the flavor of a home-baked biscuit. Storage and handling methods may also require change. Fleischmann's unsalted margarine would deteriorate in a conventional refrigerator and hence had to be frozen.

Newness in the product itself also implies new activities for those who produce, distribute, consume, or otherwise use the commodity. The processor who decides to market a soft margarine for the first time must devote effort and money to research, development, and testing. Marketing plans must be drawn up, perhaps utilizing new advertising or distribution techniques. The product may require a unique brand name or designation and its own product manager or other organizational arrangements. Such aspects of newness are, however, almost irrelevant to a food distributor. The *distributor's* interest would center around problems in freeing up refrigerated cabinet space to stock the new margarine, the extent to which it duplicates other existing margarines, and the problems of handling, warehousing, and merchandising this and other additions to his overall product line. For *consumers,* new food products may imply added convenience in use, reduction in meal preparation time, greater quality, dependability, and variety or improved taste, texture, and appearance.

3. *How New?* Anderson Clayton Company's Chiffon was the first brand of soft margarine marketed in this country. Almost universally it was regarded as new. But what of the fifth or sixth brands of similar margarines subsequently introduced? Although new to the companies that sponsored them, these brands were clearly of a lower order of newness to distributors and consumers. And what if Anderson Clayton should in the future decide to market another brand of soft margarine, similar but not identical to Chiffon? Or to introduce larger package sizes and new varieties, such as a corn

oil Chiffon to supplement the existing safflower oil Chiffon? Or to improve the existing product's formulation, perhaps renaming it New Chiffon and withdrawing the earlier version from the marketplace? All these examples are representative of different *orders* of product innovation.

4. *New When?* Chiffon was introduced to the market in late 1964. For its manufacturer, Anderson Clayton, developmental activities presumably started several months or even years before the 1964 introduction. Was the product new when the company began to develop it or when it was introduced? Further, Chiffon was first marketed on a regional basis, so that to some distributors and consumers the product was new when it was introduced to their areas in 1965. For how long does a product remain new? Is Chiffon still new in 1966 or even 1969, long after full distribution has been achieved?

As the foregoing examples illustrate, there are many dimensions of a new product. No single phrase or definition appears adequate to encompass all the relevant viewpoints and shades of meaning. What is required instead is a *set* of definitions, each reflecting different *levels of newness* and each framed with the *viewpoint* of a specific observer in mind.

The issues discussed in Chapter 1 are important to three principal groups in the economy—consumers, food processors, and food distributors. Ideally, it would be desirable to present three sets of definitions of new product, one representing the viewpoint of each group. The heterogeneity of consumers as a group, however, makes definition difficult, if not impossible. As groups, processors and distributors are each generally consistent in their interests relating to new products, whereas consumers have greatly varying perspectives. What is value to one consumer may be of little or no consequence to another. A product which is convenient to a working wife may only "taste bad" to a housewife who is at home all day, and so forth. Furthermore, as explained in Chapter 1, the data utilized in this study were derived from processors and distributors only. We have therefore utilized two sets of definitions of new products—one based on the processor's viewpoint and one based on the distributor's viewpoint. As explained in Chapter 3, we have also used estimates of the number and sales importance of new products, derived from the distributor's sales records, to represent the magnitude of product innovation in the national market. In so doing, we have assumed that the extent and timing of new product adoptions by the food chain in question were more or less representative of all food distributors in the United States, and hence adequate as a basis for estimating the magnitude of product innovation from a consumer viewpoint as well. Unfortunately, there is no meaningful way to test the validity of this assumption.

New Products from the Processor's Viewpoint

Chapters 4 and 5 of this study are concerned with the new product development and marketing activities of food processing companies. Product development and introductory marketing activities are associated with products of varying degrees of newness. For example, the development and introduction of Whip 'n Chill, a fluffy packaged dessert similar to a mousse, was presumably a far more costly, complex, and uncertain task for the General Foods Corporation than was the concurrent introduction of a new flavor to the established Jell-O line. In a sense, Whip 'n Chill can be said to represent a higher order of innovation since its development and marketing involved a more radical departure from existing company products and practices than did the additional flavor of Jell-O.

Although it seems unlikely that we could ever measure *how much* newer one product is than another, it nevertheless seems useful to classify new products into broad groupings representing different degrees of newness. The three groups used in the survey of food processors were *distinctly new products, product line extensions,* and *product improvements.*

Distinctly New Products

The highest level of processor innovation is the distinctly new product, which is defined as follows:

> *Distinctly new products* are products developed wholly or in part by the processor which are substantially different in *form, technology,* or *ingredients* from other products previously marketed by *the company.* The fact that a competitor might previously have

offered a similar product on the market does *not* disqualify its consideration as a distinctly new product. A further distinction may be drawn, however, between "pioneering" new products—here defined as the *first* and *second brands* to be introduced of a new type of product—and subsequent brands. Wherever possible, separate data are given for pioneering new products. In general, it would be expected that the introduction of a distinctly new product would be characterized by the concurrent creation of *one or more* of the following:

- Its own separate marketing plan and/or budget
- Its own separate advertising budget and distinct campaign
- Its own product manager, if applicable
- Its own profit and loss statement
- Its own brand name or product designation

The earlier example of Chiffon margarine is one which would qualify as a distinctly new product. Being a soft margarine, the product was obviously different in form from any previously marketed by the Anderson Clayton Company. In all likelihood, its introduction also was characterized by the creation of a separate marketing plan, advertising budget, product manager, and product profit and loss statement for Chiffon. Other brands of soft margarine which followed, including Blue Bonnet, Mrs. Filbert's, Kraft, Golden Glow, and Sundrop would also be regarded as distinctly new products. In each case, the sponsoring companies all had previously marketed regular margarines, but the addition of a soft margarine was new to each company concerned. Only Chiffon and the second brand to enter the market, however, would be regarded as pioneering new products.

We have designated both the first *and* second products of a new type as pioneering products because it appears that the processor who introduces the second brand typically does *not* draw upon or benefit greatly from the experience of his predecessor. In most cases, according to the processors who were interviewed in this study, development of the second brand to be introduced was begun long before the introduction of the first brand to the market. Often the second brand is introduced very shortly after the first, much too soon to permit the kind of direct emulation in processing and marketing which is commonplace later. Thus, it does not seem appropriate to view the second brand of a new type of product as simply a "me-too" product, although there are no doubt exceptions to this generalization.

Line Extensions

The next highest level of processor innovation is the line extension:

> *Line extensions* are new package sizes, flavors, or shapes of existing products; they represent *additions* to an existing line of products, and as such they employ no fundamental new technology, ingredients, or form. A line extension would not normally be expected to have its own marketing plan or budget, its own product manager (if applicable), profit and loss statement, or distinct brand name; it may, or may not, have its own advertising campaign or budget, but if so, these would normally be employed only at the time of its introduction.

The introduction of line extensions is a frequent occurrence, since many successful distinctly new products are subsequently followed by additional package sizes and/or flavors. The new flavor of Jell-O previously cited is one example, while the addition of a 2-pound jar of Skippy peanut butter is another.

Product Improvements

Product improvements, usually the lowest level of processor innovation, are defined as follows:

> *Product improvements* are changes in existing products, such as changes in ingredients, appearance, taste, or texture. A change in packaging would also be regarded as a product improvement *if* the change resulted in a package with improved *performance characteristics*. Since a product improvement involves an "amended" product, the form of the product existing prior to the change is presumed to be withdrawn from the market.

Product improvements are probably the most frequent type of processor innovation. Almost every product which endures in the market for a susbtantial period of time undergoes some improvement. For the most part, individual improvements are often unnoticed, although the total effect of many creeping changes in a product may be substantial, if not essential for competitive sur-

vival. Today's brands of peanut butter, for example, are more nutritious, smoother in texture, and more flavorful than their predecessors. Oil separation has been virtually eliminated and the tendency of peanut butter to stick to the roof of the mouth has been
minimized. All are examples of product improvements.

New Products from the Distributor's Viewpoint

Chapter 3 of this study deals with the nature and extent of product innovation in selected food product categories. Estimates of the
extent of new product introductions are based on an analysis of a
large food chain's sales in each of the categories for the period
1954–1964. The chain's records, however, are not readily amenable
to the sort of definitional standards established for the processor
survey. In analyzing these data, what is required instead is a set
of definitional standards suited specifically to the viewpoint of the
distributor.

The analysis in Chapter 3 provides estimates of the number and
sales importance of three classes of new products, representing
three different levels of newness. In descending order, these are
new *types* of products, new *brands*, and new *items*.

New Types

The highest level of innovation, from the distributor's viewpoint,
is the new type of product, defined as follows:

> *New types* of products are those substantially different in form,
> basic ingredients, and/or method of use in the home from any
> other product previously stocked by the retailer. A new type of
> product may be added under the umbrella of an existing brand
> name, or it may also have an entirely new brand name.

Examples of new types of products are Awake, the first synthetic
fruit juice concentrate; instant-blending flour; and soft margarine.
In each case, the risks and implications for the distributor stocking
such products are at their highest level. Because consumers have
had no direct prior experience with new types of products, their
sales, profit potential, and effect on existing products in the line
are extremely uncertain.

It is helpful to relate the highest order of distributor innovation to the comparable level for that of the processor. In general, a *new type* of product is also a distinctly new product to the processor who supplies it. Awake orange juice, Gold Medal Wondra instant-blending flour, and Chiffon margarine all represent new types of products and would similarly be regarded by their manufacturers as distinctly new products. Not all distinctly new products, however, represent new types to the distributor. In the early 1960's, for example, Lever Brothers began to market its Good Luck brand of dehydrated potatoes—a distinctly new product for the company. A chain which added the Lever product to its line at that time, however, would in all probability already have been carrying a number of similar dehydrated potato products and would not consider the addition as a new type.

New Brands

Good Luck dehydrated potatoes would be regarded by the distributor as a new brand:

> *New brands* are manufacturers' or distributors' brands not previously carried by the retailer on other products *within the same category*. A brand may be regarded as new despite the fact that the same brand has previously been carried on products in *other* categories, provided it is being stocked in the category under examination for the first time.

Because their interests are divergent, there is really no basis for comparing this level of distributor innovation with any single level of processor innovation. New brands to the distributor may be distinctly new products to the processors, or they may be line extensions. A distributor may decide to fill out his line of liquid dietary foods by adding selected flavors of a new brand, all of which represent line extensions to the processor's original distinctly new product. Good Luck, on the other hand, would be both a distributor's new brand and a processor's distinctly new product.

New Items

> *New items* are *any* articles or products added to the chain's stock for the first time. A new item may be a new package size, flavor, or variety of an existing brand, or a new brand. In this study,

minor *changes*, in package size, shape, or design (for example, the substitution of an 8¾-ounce package for an 8-ounce package) are, however, *excluded* from consideration as new items.

Any addition to a distributor's product line is regarded as a new item. This is the broadest possible definition of new products.

Unlike the set of definitions used in the processor survey, it should be noted that the classifications used in the analysis of chain sales data are *not* mutually exclusive. That is, a new *item* may (or may not) also be a new *brand* and could further be a *new type* of product. Every new type of product and every new brand, however, are also new items.

In practice, the greatest proportion of new items are additional flavors, sizes, and varieties of existing products. These new items correspond to the processor's product line extensions.

Borderline Cases

The definitions stated above provide the basis for classifying new products into groups, depending on the level or degree of newness which it represents.

Even this classification is not completely unequivocal; there are borderline cases, which, in the final analysis, must be assigned to one of the three categories somewhat arbitrarily. For example, when a processor of biscuits, cookies, and crackers introduces a new type of cookie, is this a distinctly new product or a product line extension? An argument can be made either way: on the one hand, such a product may be substantially different in form and in ingredients from existing products; in some cases, difficult technical problems must be solved before a cookie can be produced on a large scale at reasonable cost. On the other hand, *most* new cookies and crackers are produced in much the same way as existing versions and are essentially new *combinations* of the same basic types of ingredients. For these reasons, a new cookie product might well be considered a line extension, more like a new *flavor* than like a basically new *type* of product.

No satisfactory way could be devised to define a distinctly new product so as to avoid borderline cases altogether. In the analysis of the results of the processor survey, the authors have used their own best judgments, taking into account all the circumstances, in classifying some products as either distinctly new products or product line extensions.

Borderline questions of categorization were not so common in the historical analysis of food chain sales data. No ambiguities were encountered in identifying new items and brands, but there is a certain element of judgment as to what constitutes a new *type* of product. In most instances, new types are self-evident. Nutritional cereals, for example, now constitute about 12% of all cold cereal sales and clearly represent a new type. But what of the more recent cereals containing freeze-dried fruit—are they a new type or simply an additional variety of existing cereal products?

Once again, the authors have necessarily resorted to their own best judgments in resolving the borderline cases.

One final issue remains unresolved. Given that we can classify a product as new in the sense of any of the definitions above, the question still exists as to *how long* this same product should be considered to remain new. The principal reason for interest in new products is that they differ in various ways from other, more mature products. Presumably, therefore, we would consider a product as new as long as it continues to exhibit differences in patterns of sales, prices, and competitive behavior.

In general, the results of this study and others suggest that, in terms of sales patterns, profitability, and promotional activities, food products exhibit different behavior during their first two years in the marketplace.

Consequently, in Chapter 3 we treat products as new for a period of two years following introduction.

CHAPTER 3

Product Innovation in
Selected Food Product Categories

AT THE TURN of the century the average American family's diet was monotonous. Meats, fruits, vegetables, and milk had to be produced locally, and many commodities were not available at all during the winter months. The housewife of 1900 spent many long hours in the kitchen.

By contrast, today's market basket is far more nutritious and varied than that of a half century ago. Most commodities are available year-round in fresh or frozen form, and much of the preparation that used to be done at home can now be purchased "built-in" to the food product. These changes have largely been achieved by technological development.

In this chapter, a brief historical account of product innovation in each of the food categories covered by this study is presented. The purpose of providing these capsule summaries is to document the tremendous and varied scope of change that has occurred in food products, and to illustrate by example the historical nature of product innovation. Primary attention is directed to the period since 1945, not only because of its recency but also because it appears that the adoption of innovation as a way of life is essentially a post-World War II development.

Format of Product Category Histories

For each of the product categories covered in this chapter, two types of information are presented: a historical account of major product innovations, and statistical estimates of the *extent* of new product introductions during the period 1954–1964.

The historical summaries are based largely on published sources of information. The statistical data were derived from an analysis of the warehouse shipment records of Grand Valley Markets, as described in Chapter 1. The Grand Valley Markets warehouse shipments figures have been utilized to determine the *number and proportion of total product* category sales accounted for by:

1. *New items* introduced since the preceding time period;
2. *New brands* introduced since the preceding time period; and
3. *New types of products* introduced since the preceding time period.

All these data have been computed for each even-numbered year between 1954 and 1964, i.e., 1954, 1956, etc. Thus, the data given for each year represent sales of new items, brands, or types introduced during a two-year period. The data are presented primarily in terms of products introduced during a two-year period preceding a given date because it seems appropriate to regard a product as new for about two years, more or less, after its introduction. As shown in Chapters 4 and 5, it is during the first two years that a product's sales, cost, and profit performance differs most significantly from that of established products. Moreover, virtually all *unsuccessful* products are withdrawn within the first two years; if a product survives this long, it may be regarded as being established for an indefinite period of time.

Items, brands, and types added and dropped during each two-year interval were identified by comparing the Grand Valley warehouse catalog for each period with that of the corresponding period two years earlier. Since some items were both added *and* dropped during each two-year period, the data presented in the tables below understate the total amount of new product activity somewhat.

Data are also presented for each product category in terms of over-all changes in product assortments between 1954 and 1964. These figures were derived from a comparison of the 1964 warehouse shipment records with the 1954 records.

To facilitate understanding of the Grand Valley Markets data, the presentation format may be explained briefly here. For each category, a table is given showing:

1. The number of items stocked (i.e., listed in the Grand Valley warehouse catalog) during each year.

2. An index of dollar sales volume for the product category. As explained in Chapter 1, the Grand Valley Markets sales figures have been adjusted so as to allow for the effects of changes in the number of stores operated by the chain.
3. The percentage of product category sales in each year accounted for by (a) new items, (b) new brands, and (c) new types of products, introduced during the preceding two years. Also, for 1964 the percentage of annual sales accounted for by items, brands, and types introduced since 1954 is shown.

To illustrate the manner in which these estimates have been developed and used, refer to Table 3-1 (page 37) which shows the figures for cold breakfast cereals. The first column of this table shows the total number of items stocked: 32 in 1954, 44 in 1956, and so on, increasing steadily to 67 in 1964. The item count reflects *all* types, brands, package sizes, and other product variations within the cold cereal category. Consequently, the increase in number of items stocked is at best a crude indicator of new product activity. This point is discussed further in Chapter 6.

The second column of Table 3-1 shows that cold cereal sales volume increased substantially during the 10-year period, reaching a level in 1964 of 2.3 times greater than in 1954. Changes in total product category sales reflect many factors besides new product additions, such as price changes and increased consumption of older products. But, as will be shown in the last section of this chapter, there is generally a fairly close relationship between the extent of new product activity in a category and its rate of sales growth.

The last three columns of Table 3-1 present estimates of the proportion of total category sales in each year accounted for by items, brands, and types introduced during the preceding two years. For example, in 1956, 28% of Grand Valley's total cold cereal sales represented new *items*; nearly 7% of sales was accounted for by new *brands*; and almost 11% was contributed by new *types* of cereals. These figures are not, of course, mutually exclusive. New item sales, by definition, include sales of new brands and types. New brands may or may not be new types, and new types may be introduced under existing brand names and/or under new brands. In 1956 the percentage of sales accounted for by new types was greater than that attributable to new brands; most of the new-type cereals introduced in that year (which were "nutritional" products) were, in fact, sold under established brand names such as Kellogg and Post.

The bottom row of figures in Table 3-1 shows the proportion of annual sales in 1964 accounted for by all the items, brands, and types added to Grand Valley's assortment since 1954. Thus, in 1964, two-thirds of the year's sales was contributed by items not stocked in 1954; only 6% represented new brands, while 13% was attributable to new types of cereals. Since only one new type of cereal was introduced during the decade—nutritional cereals in 1956—the figure for 1964 includes the same items covered by the 1956 figure, in addition to several other brands and items in the nutritional subcategory which were added after 1956. In none of the product categories covered by the study was more than one new type of product introduced during the 10-year period.

The same presentation format has been used for all the product categories, as shown in Tables 3-2 through 3-21.

Breakfast Cereals—Cold (Ready-to-Eat)

The cold cereal industry had its origins with the vegetarians and food faddists of the 19th century. The modern industry owes its beginnings primarily to two such men, C. W. Post and William Keith Kellogg.

In the 1890's, while a patient at the Battle Creek Sanitarium, Post was exposed to a variety of cereal-based foods and sensed commercial possibilities for the products. In 1897 he founded the Postum Cereal Company and began the marketing and promotion of Postum (a cereal) and later of Grape-Nuts. W. K. Kellogg, meanwhile, was an employee at the same Battle Creek Sanitarium. While working there, Kellogg discovered a means of producing corn flakes. In 1906 he left the health center to form the Battle Creek Toasted Corn Flake Company, the forerunner of today's Kellogg Company.

Ready-to-eat cereals soon gained wide popularity. Between 1902 and 1904, 42 cereal companies sprang up in Battle Creek. Nearly all of these subsequently failed. Secrecy and patent protection, together with the high costs of processing equipment and of cereal promotion, led to a concentration of the industry among a few manufacturers. In 1964 six companies accounted for almost 98% of all retail sales.

By 1947 cold cereal consumption had reached 601 million pounds, or about 4.1 pounds per person. Sales declined slightly in 1948, and there were indications that per capita consumption had reached a ceiling. Then in 1949 General Foods' Post Division introduced Sugar Crisp, the first of a new class of cold cereal products that were presweetened by a coating of sugar. Other manufacturers followed quickly with presweetened brands. By 1964 at least 21 presweetened cereal brands were available, and the category accounted for almost 26% of retail cereal sales.

In 1955 a second new class of cereal products came to market with the introduction by the Kellogg Company of Special K, a product especially high in protein and other vitamins. Special K was an immediate success, but other manufacturers were in this instance somewhat slower to retaliate—not until 1958 was a second brand of nutritional cereal introduced. By 1964 at least six nutritional cereals had been introduced, and they accounted for almost 10% of all cereal sales.

The impact of the new nutritional products is reflected in the cold cereal sales history of the Grand Valley chain, as shown in Table 3-1. In the introductory year of 1956 the new type of product accounted for 10.9% of sales; by 1964 it had grown to 13.4% of sales at Grand Valley. During the 10-year period total cold cereal sales increased 2.3 times and the number of items stocked more than doubled. By 1964 items added since 1954 accounted for over two-thirds of Grand Valley's cereal sales.

Between 1947 and 1964 cold cereal consumption in the United States grew in both absolute and per capita terms. From a 1947 level of 602 millions pounds, sales had increased to over 1.1 billion pounds by 1964. The growth in per capita consumption, however, was almost entirely due to the two new types of cereals, presweetened and nutritional. Regular cereal consumption in 1964 was 4.2 pounds per capita (as it was in 1947), but presweetened and nutritional cereals added another 1.7 pounds to the 1964 consumption level.

In 1964 General Foods' Post Division introduced still another

TABLE 3-1

GRAND VALLEY MARKETS

Cold (Ready-to-Eat) Cereal Sales: 1954–1964

Year	Number of Items Stocked	Index of Sales Volume	% of Annual Sales Accounted for by: New Items	New Brands	New Types
			(Introduced during preceding 2 years)		
1954	32	100	—	—	—
1956	44	135	28.2%	6.7%	10.9%
1958	47	168	18.9	0	0
1960	53	200	17.0	0	0
1962	63	216	16.2	0	0
1964	67	231	22.0	0	0
			(Introduced since 1954)		
1964 vs. 1954			67.8%	6.2%	13.4%

new group of cereal products containing freeze-dried fruits. The Kellogg Company followed soon after with similar products. Expectations for freeze-dried fruit in cereals were high, but in early 1966 their future was still very much in doubt. To quote one trade source, "Almost without exception, they haven't lived up to either conservative predictions or early promise." [1]

Breakfast Cereals—Hot

Hot cereals, requiring preparation before eating, have been known to man for centuries. The dry fruit of members of the grass family, cereal products have been used by Americans since the early settlement days when they constituted a major share of the family diet.

For many years prior to the 1960's the consumption of hot cereals has been in decline, primarily due to the increased popularity of the more convenient ready-to-eat cereals. Between 1947 and

[1] "Ready-To-Eat Cereals Race for Facings as Sales Increase," *Food Topics*, February 1966, p. 44.

1964 total United States hot cereal sales fell from just over 465 million pounds to 386 million pounds. The decline represents a 37% drop in per capita consumption.

Hot cereal sales for the Grand Valley chain are shown in Table 3-2 and reflect the low level of new product activity in this declining food category. Between 1954 and 1964 sales volume fell slightly, while the number of items stocked remained almost con-

TABLE 3-2

GRAND VALLEY MARKETS

Hot Cereal Sales: 1954–1964

Year	Number of Items Stocked	Index of Sales Volume	% of Annual Sales Accounted for by:		
			New Items	New Brands	New Types
			(Introduced during preceding 2 years)		
1954	17	100	—	—	—
1956	20	103	6.0%	1.6%	0
1958	19	103	11.0	0	0
1960	19	97	4.0	0	0
1962	21	95	7.4	0	0
1964	19	93	0	0	0
			(Introduced since 1954)		
1964 vs. 1954			18.5%	0	0

stant. The few new items that were added were of relatively minor importance; in 1964 over 80% of sales were still accounted for by items Grand Valley had been stocking for at least a decade. In 1956 two new brands were added, but their combined effect was so small that both had been dropped by 1964.

In 1964 the leading manufacturer in the field, Quaker Oats Company, introduced a new "instant" oatmeal product requiring no cooking, only the addition of hot water. Clearly intended to provide the added convenience demanded by modern housewives, the product and others like it represented an attempt to stem the steady decline of hot cereals in past years.

Cake Mixes

The idea of a baking mix—a flour-based mix containing most of the ingredients necessary for preparing a finished baked product—is not a new one. As early as the 1880's pancake or griddle mix was sold under the Aunt Jemima brand. It was a half century later, however, before this same mix concept was applied to cakes. In 1931 P. Duff and Sons, Pittsburgh molasses makers, introduced a gingerbread mix and became the pioneer in the field.

Cake mixes did not achieve immediate widespread popularity. Perhaps the severe economic conditions of the 1930's did not lend themselves to the use of cake mix products. Another explanation has been suggested by psychologist Dr. Ernest Dichter, who attributed the slow acceptance of cake mixes to a "hostility" on the part of housewives who allegedly considered the mixes an affront to their own culinary skills.

Whatever caused a slow beginning, there seems little doubt that the advent of World War II brought with it the circumstances to start the cake mix boom. During the war years wider employment of women outside the home created a demand for easy-to-prepare meals. Sugar rationing and shortening shortages discouraged home baking. Between 1942 and 1946 cake mix sales increased 230%, and by 1947 the industry included over 200 firms.[2] "Those were the days," said one industry executive, "when cake mixes were miracles; when using them was like having the essence of the modern world in your kitchen." [3]

The immediate postwar years brought the beginning of a host of new flavors and varieties that were to be introduced in the years to come. By 1954 it was estimated that white and chocolate cake mixes accounted for only 55% of industry sales, as opposed to almost 100% just a few years before.[4]

The growing postwar enthusiasm for cake mixes was reflected in industry sales figures. Between 1949 and 1955 retail unit sales

---

[2] *Tide*, May 21, 1948.
[3] "Have Cake Mix Sales Hit a Plateau?", *Printers' Ink*, December 9, 1960, p. 9.
[4] The Curtis Publishing Company, "Market for Baking Mixes," Library Report No. 61–9, August 18, 1961, p. 5.

almost trebled, from 6.8 million to 17.1 million cases. After 1955 the rate of growth was much slower. Although population contributed slightly to growth to a 1964 retail sales level of 20.6 million cases, per capita consumption of cake mixes has been virtually stable since 1956.

The high level of new product activity in this category is demonstrated by the sales of cake mix products at Grand Valley Mar-

TABLE 3-3

GRAND VALLEY MARKETS

Cake Mix Sales: 1954–1964

Year	Number of Items Stocked	Index of Sales Volume	% of Annual Sales Accounted for by:		
			New Items	New Brands	New Types
			(Introduced during preceding 2 years)		
1954	39	100	—	—	—
1956	77	161	43.1%	6.9%	0
1958	86	166	32.2	0.3	0
1960	96	164	46.4	34.9	0
1962	122	164	37.4	5.1	0
1964	108	159	27.4	2.1	0
			(Introduced since 1954)		
1964 vs. 1954			82.7%	35.8%	0

kets, as shown in Table 3-3. In each year new items introduced during the previous two-year period accounted for at least one-fourth, and sometimes nearly half, of the total sales volume. By 1964 items that had been introduced since 1954 constituted 82.7% of total sales. The number of items stocked grew from 39 in 1954 to 108 in 1964, but this growth only partially reflects the level of new product activity during the period. Not indicated on the table is the fact that the net increase of 69 items was made up by the *addition* of no less than 207 items and the dropping of 138 items during the 10-year interval.

While most new cake mix items at Grand Valley were introduced by brands previously carried by the chain, the decision to add Procter and Gamble's Duncan Hines brand in 1960 had a profound effect. The only new brand added by Grand Valley in that year, Duncan Hines immediately captured 34.9% of the chain's cake mix volume.

Canned Vegetables

The experimental work of a Frenchman, Nicolas Appert, provided the beginnings of today's canning industry. Appert's experiments on food preservation were begun in 1795 when France, under Napoleon, was fighting most of the other nations in Europe. Needing transportable food for his widespread armies, Napoleon had offered a prize of 12,000 francs to anyone finding a suitable method of preserving food. Appert discovered that he could keep foods for long periods of time by cooking them, sealing them airtight, then cooking them again. In 1810, after 15 years of work, he published his results in the treatise, *The Art of Preserving All Kinds of Animal and Vegetable Substances for Several Years*, and was awarded Napoleon's prize.

Appert used glass containers, but soon after "tin" cans (actually, steel with a coating of tin) became prevalent. Commercial canning of many substances, including vegetables, followed quickly. In the United States the first successful canning operation was established by William Underwood in 1819.

The ensuing century and a half has seen many changes in canning processes. New machinery and techniques have greatly increased productivity, and research has improved the flavor, appearance, and nutritive content of canned vegetables. There are few canned vegetables on the market today, however, that have not been available for many years. Since World War II canned vegetables have faced intense competition from newer forms of processed vegetables, primarily frozen and dehydrated.

Different segments of the market, however, do not appear to have been uniformly affected by the new competition. Per capita consumption of canned peas, for example, declined by 32% between 1947 and 1964 (in terms of unit retail sales), while canned corn showed a 10% *increase* in per capita consumption during the same time period. In 1964 the total market for all canned vegetables was estimated at $1.25 billion, an increase from the 1950 market of $782 million.[5] That increase, however, was probably accounted for by population growth and price increases during the same period of time.

Canned vegetable sales data for Grand Valley Markets were not analyzed because of the great number of items and brands involved and because of the known fact that no basically new types of products were introduced during the period 1954–1964.

Dehydrated Potatoes

As early as 1907 a patent was taken out in this country for a potato dehydrating process. The first widely used dehydration process was developed, however, as a result of military needs during World War II. To save shipping space and simplify handling of potatoes, both the British and the Americans turned to dehydration. The result was a palatable, but not too flavorful, instant potato product.

Remembering their wartime experiences, few American service veterans would have given dehydrated potatoes a chance, but the British firm of Reckitt & Colman believed the product would sell and assigned the marketing job to its American subsidiary, R. T. French Company. French introduced dehydrated potatoes in several U.S. cities in 1946; the product was slow to grow in its early years and gained little more than a toehold in the market.

Two subsequent developments, however, spurred sales greatly. In 1954, while other major companies had entered the market (the first, General Foods, in 1952) and were concentrating on improved products, French developed a nitrogen atmosphere package. The new package not only extended shelf life but permitted the sale of dehydrated potatoes for the first time in hot and humid areas of the country where, in its older package, the product had deteriorated rapidly.

Perhaps the most important breakthrough came in 1956 when the U.S. Department of Agriculture's Eastern Utilization Laboratory, after three years of research, developed a *flaked* dehydrated

---

[5] *Food Topics,* issues of September 1951 and September 1965.

potato, as opposed to the *granular* product previously used. The flaked product offered several advantages. Reconstituting qualities, flavor, and texture were reputedly better; and the manufacturing process was simpler and required less machinery and equipment. The flaked process also permitted use of low-solid content potatoes grown in the eastern part of the country, whereas the granular method required high-quality Idaho potatoes.

Most established manufacturers switched to the new flaked process, and several new competitors entered the market shortly afterward. By 1959 only three manufacturers produced the granular dehydrated potato. French, the market leader, was one of them. Consumer acceptance was enthusiastic, too, with retail sales reaching 62.5 million pounds in 1959. By 1964, 15 U.S. companies were producing dehydrated potatoes, with total retail sales of 133 million pounds; institutional sales to restaurants, hotels, and so on were estimated at twice that amount.

In 1959 and 1960 the rapidly expanding dehydrated potato market began to experience the infusion of new specialty products. Scalloped potatoes, potatoes au gratin, baked potatoes, potato pancakes, and numerous other varieties in dehydrated form appeared on the market to supplement the old standby mashed potato.

The growing popularity of dehydrated potato products in the late 1950's was slow to be felt at the Grand Valley Market chain, as shown in Table 3-4. From 1954 to 1958 only one size of a single brand was stocked. In 1960 new items, of both the regular mashed and new specialty types, accounted for 71.8% of total sales. Specialty products alone comprised 37% of category sales in that year. By 1964 items new since 1954 accounted for 83.4% of sales, with new brands accounting for 59.6%. In the 10-year period since 1954 total deyhdrated potato sales had increased by more than 1,700%, with the new specialty products comprising almost half of the 1964 volume.

Starting with a single item in 1958, the number of dehydrated potato items stocked by Grand Valley had grown to 13 by 1964. If the Grand Valley experience is representative, however, the manufacturers' race to get new items into retailers' shelves during the period was not without its casualties. The net increase of 12

TABLE 3-4

GRAND VALLEY MARKETS

Dehydrated Potato Sales: 1954–1964

Year	Number of Items Stocked	Index of Sales Volume	% of Annual Sales Accounted for by:		
			New Items	New Brands	New Types
			(Introduced during preceding 2 years)		
1954	1	100	—	—	—
1956	1	179	0	0	0
1958	1	1,000	0	0	0
1960	10	1,397	71.8%	71.8%	37.0%
1962	11	1,726	35.4	0	0
1964	13	1,804	51.9	12.9	0
			(Introduced since 1954)		
1964 vs. 1954			83.4%	59.6%	46.7%

items stocked was made up of the addition of 21 items and the dropping of 9; that is, for approximately every two new items added, one was dropped. No fewer than seven different brands of dehydrated potatoes were being stocked by Grand Valley in 1964.

Evaporated and Condensed Milk

Along with the rest of the canning industry, the evaporated milk industry had its beginnings in the experimental work of the Frenchman, Nicolas Appert, in the early 19th century. Appert was the first to evaporate and preserve milk by heat in sealed containers. His process was a crude one; by boiling at high temperatures in the open air, he unknowingly destroyed much of the nutritive content of the milk. He did, however, demonstrate that concentrating milk was practical.

The first commercially produced canned milk product was a sweetened condensed milk developed by Gail Borden in the 1850's. *Unsweetened* evaporated milk, however, required a sterilizing process without sugar and was first developed by the Swiss, John Mey-

TABLE 3-5

GRAND VALLEY MARKETS

Evaporated and Condensed Milk Sales: 1954–1964

Year	Number of Items Stocked	Index of Sales Volume	% of Annual Sales Accounted for by:		
			New Items	New Brands	New Types
			(Introduced during preceding 2 years)		
1954	8	100	—	—	—
1956	8	103	5.2%	5.2%	0
1958	7	103	0	0	0
1960	6	90	0	0	0
1962	9	79	15.0	15.0	0
1964	8	68	0	0	0
			(Introduced since 1954)		
1964 vs. 1954			26.8%	26.8%	0

enberg. Unable to attract interest for the product in his home country, Meyenberg emigrated to the United States. In 1885 his Helvita Milk Condensing Company in Highland, Illinois, became the first in the world to produce and market an evaporated milk product.

The original development of both evaporated and sweetened condensed milk was spurred by a need for storable, transportable, and hygienically safe milk. For many decades evaporated and condensed milk were the only products available to meet such a need. The growing availability of refrigeration facilities after 1920 gradually reduced the need for canned milk products. More recently dried milk products (both dairy and synthetic), together with specially prepared infant milk formulas, have gained greatly increased acceptance. As a result sales of evaporated and condensed milk have been declining steadily. Total United States retail sales of $238 million in 1964 represented a 42% drop in per capita consumption since 1947.

The relative decline of canned milk popularity is reflected in the sales experience of Grand Valley Markets, as shown in Table 3-5. Between 1954 and 1964 volume fell by almost one-third, and in only two years (1956 and 1962) were any new items added.

Both of the new items were low-priced packers' brands. By 1964, 73.2% of sales was still accounted for by items and brands that Grand Valley had been carrying for at least ten years.

All-Purpose Flour

Bronze tablets dating from the ninth century before Christ depict the grinding of wheat into flour, and Assyrian and Egyptian tombs along the Nile River contain murals showing the grinding of flour and the making of bread. While its exact origins are not clear, flour has for centuries past been one of the basic staples in man's diet.

Different wheats result in flours of different properties. Hard wheat flour, for example, is better for bread, but lower protein flours result in more tender products, better for cakes. All-purpose (or "family") flour is essentially a compromise—a blend of different wheats to meet, insofar as possible, all of a family's needs.

Changes in flour products have tended to take the form of gradual improvements to existing types. Presifting of flour and vitamin enrichment are examples of such improvements. In 1963, however, General Mills introduced what the company described as "the first truly new form of flour in 4,000 years." The product, Gold Medal Wondra, was an instant-blending all-purpose flour. In granular form, it was free-pouring like salt and dust-free compared to regular flour.

Gold Medal Wondra was the result of a seemingly unrelated type of research. Several years previously paper manufacturers had asked General Mills to develop a powdered guar gum that would not lump in water, and it was the successful research in this area that led to the development of instant-blending flour.

For some years prior to the 1960's consumption of all-purpose flour had been declining. Prepared baking mixes, frozen baked products, and similar convenience foods have all reduced the incidence of home baking "from scratch." Between 1953 and 1964 total United States retail sales of all-purpose flour declined from 3.4 billion pounds to 2.7 billion pounds. Instant-blending flour seems to have been incapable of reverting this trend. Despite the subsequent introduction of similar products by two other

major millers (Pillsbury and International Milling), instant-blending flours had, by the end of 1964, captured only 4% of a steadily
declining market.

Sales of all-purpose flour at the Grand Valley chain are illustrated in Table 3-6. Most immediately noticeable is the effect of
the new instant-blending brands which were first stocked in 1964.
These brands accounted for 10.7% of 1964 sales, considerably

TABLE 3-6

GRAND VALLEY MARKETS

All-Purpose Flour Sales: 1954–1964

Year	Number of Items Stocked	Index of Sales Volume	% of Annual Sales Accounted for by:		
			New Items	New Brands	New Types
			(Introduced during preceding 2 years)		
1954	11	100	—	—	—
1956	11	111	0	0	0
1958	10	109	0.9%	0	0
1960	14	114	15.9	12.8%	0
1962	15	124	8.8	0	0
1964	21	131	15.4	2.8	10.7%
			(Introduced since 1954)		
1964 vs. 1954			34.3%	11.9%	10.7%

above the national average. New brands introduced since 1954 (a
strong regional brand was added in 1960) comprised only 11.9%
of 1964 sales, although new items (including instant blending)
added in the same interval accounted for 34.3% of 1964 volume.
The increase in the number of items stocked is attributable chiefly
to the addition of the new regional brand (in three package sizes)
and of the instant-blending items.

Frozen Dinners and Specialties

With increasing consumer demands for convenience in food
and, concurrently, with the growing acceptance of frozen food in

TABLE 3-7

GRAND VALLEY MARKETS

Frozen Dinners and Specialties Sales: 1954–1964

Year	Number of Items Stocked	Index of Sales Volume	% of Annual Sales Accounted for by:		
			New Items	New Brands	New Types*
			(Introduced during preceding 2 years)		
1954	15	100	—	—	—
1956	N.A.	N.A.	N.A.	N.A.	N.A.
1958	66	364	87.7%†	80.1%†	N.A.
1960	99	394	37.7	18.8	N.A.
1962	118	451	39.6	14.5	N.A.
1964	132	483	28.1	8.3	N.A.
			(Introduced since 1954)		
1964 vs. 1954			87.7%	54.6%	N.A.

* Frozen dinners and specialties includes a wide variety of products of many different "types," e.g., frozen complete dinners, entrees of various kinds, and specialty foods such as pizza. Many new items have been introduced since 1954, but in most cases these items cannot be classified unequivocally as new *types* of products because they differ only slightly in form, ingredients, and processing methods from existing products. Consequently, no attempt has been made to estimate the proportion of annual sales accounted for by new types of products in this category.

† Because 1956 data were not available, figures for new items and brands in 1958 refer to items added in the *four*-year interval 1954–1958.

the postwar era, it was perhaps natural that the industry should respond by introducing a whole new class of prepared food products. Frozen dinners and specialties encompass a vast range of products in prepared or semiprepared form—dinners, meat pies, baked goods, casseroles, ethnic foods. Packaged in a wide variety of cardboard, aluminum, and plastic bag combinations, this collection of prepared foods has grown from its postwar start to an estimated 1964 sales volume of $1.2 billion, almost one-fourth of all frozen food sales.[6]

---

[6] *Quick Frozen Foods*, October 1965, p. 135.

The rapid growth of frozen dinner and specialty products is reflected in Table 3-7, showing the experience of the Grand Valley chain. While sales volume grew by a factor of almost five, the chain had to provide freezer cabinet space for 132 items in 1964, as opposed to only 15 in 1954. Not revealed by the table is the constant turmoil of new product activity during this growth period. For example, during the 10-year period Grand Valley at one time or another had stocked a total of 67 different brands of dinner and specialty products. Some were not successful, but in 1964 no fewer than 42 brands were represented in the Grand Valley selection. During this period some 232 new items were added, while 115 were dropped.

By 1964 new items introduced since 1954 accounted for 87.6% of frozen dinner and specialty sales at Grand Valley. A relatively lower 54.6% of 1964 volume was contributed by new brands. In fact, since 1958 the old brands have steadily *increased* their share of the category's sales, primarily by offering an ever-expanding variety of products under the umbrella of a common brand name.

Frozen Juice Concentrates

During World War II National Research Corporation of Boston, which had perfected a high-vacuum process for the production of penicillin and blood plasma, began to experiment with using the same techniques to manufacture an orange juice powder. The incentive for their research was an expressed desire by the U.S. Army for such a powder and a standing order of 500,000 pounds for the company that could produce it cheaply and in quantity. Forming a subsidiary, Vacuum Foods Corporation (later Minute Maid Corporation), the company built a pilot plant in Plymouth, Florida, in 1944 and had a full-scale plant under construction at the time of the war's end in 1945. With the termination of the war, however, the Army cancelled its contract.

Vacuum Foods next looked to market their orange powder abroad, but a universal dollar shortage made this prospect unattractive. While the powder made a juice at least as flavorful as ordinary canned juice, the cost was not competitive in domestic markets and it soon became apparent that the powdered product could not succeed. At this point scientists at the Florida Citrus Commission suggested to the company the idea of stopping the manufacturing process short of the point where the concentrate was converted to a powder, then adding back regular fresh juice to restore the natural flavor and appearance qualities otherwise lost. In this form the product would have to be quick-frozen for preservation.

Under the Minute Maid brand the frozen orange concentrate was introduced to the domestic market in April 1946. That year, however, was one in which a host of inferior frozen foods had been introduced by marginal packers, and consumers were generally antagonistic toward the industry. Concentrate sales in the first year were disappointingly low. Buoyed by a fresh infusion of capital, however, Vacuum Foods persisted in its efforts and the product began to gain widespread acceptance. Other flavor varieties of juice concentrate, utilizing similar processing technology, were soon added to most manufacturers' product lines. In 1950 industry sales of frozen orange juice concentrate had grown to 15.3 million gallons and by 1957 to 63.0 million gallons.[7]

In late 1963 General Foods Corporation startled a now "mature" frozen concentrate industry with the introduction of Awake, a synthetic frozen orange concentrate made with artificial flavorings and having no real fruit content. Sweeter in flavor than the regular orange concentrate, Awake was backed with an estimated annual promotion and advertising expenditure of $5 million (as opposed to $4.5 million being spent by the entire orange juice industry). By the end of 1965 the synthetic product had captured a 14% share of the orange juice drink business.[8]

Consumer preference for a sweeter orange juice was apparently at least part of the explanation of Awake's success. In July 1965 the natural juice industry responded to the synthetic challenge when Minute Maid became the first to market a sweetened orange concentrate. This product required a change in Florida state legislation which had hitherto prohibited adding sugar to natural orange juice.

---

[7] U.S. Department of Agriculture, *Consumer Purchases of Citrus Fruit, Juices, Drinks, and Other Products*, issues of January 1951 and January 1958.
[8] "Orange Men Get Caught in Squeeze," *Business Week*, December 4, 1965, p. 156.

As shown in Table 3-8, the synthetic type of product captured 6.8% of all frozen juice concentrate sales at Grand Valley Markets in 1964. Overall, new items introduced since 1954 comprised 67.5% of the chain's 1964 volume in this category. Apart from the synthetic juice, most of the new items were pack-

TABLE 3-8

GRAND VALLEY MARKETS

Frozen Juice Concentrate Sales: 1954–1964

Year	Number of Items Stocked	Index of Sales Volume	% of Annual Sales Accounted for by:		
			New Items	New Brands	New Types
			(*Introduced during preceding 2 years*)		
1954	15	100	—	—	—
1956	N.A.	N.A.	N.A.	N.A.	N.A.
1958	23	143	43.3%*	24.0%*	0
1960	28	148	24.5	21.4	0
1962	32	151	21.8	3.6	0
1964	42	131	16.0	12.2	6.8%
			(*Introduced since 1954*)		
1964 vs. 1954			67.5%	28.8%	6.8%

* Because 1956 data were not available, figures for new items and brands in 1958 refer to items added in the *four*-year interval 1954–1958.

ers' brands and new sizes. New brands introduced since 1954 accounted for almost 30% of the 1964 volume.

Frozen Vegetables

As early as 1842 a patent was granted in England for freezing of foods by immersion in salt and brine. Other patents, in both Great Britain and the United States, followed at intervals throughout the 19th century, but it was not until the development of mechanical refrigeration that widespread application of freezing became possible.

Much of the credit for today's frozen foods industry belongs to Clarence Birdseye, the first man to produce frozen foods for retail sale. Birdseye, while on a government expedition to Labrador, was impressed by the quality of food frozen naturally in Labrador's frigid climate and foresaw the possibility of commercial development. Returning from Labrador in 1917, he began work in the development of equipment and processes for fast freezing of fish. By 1924, having overcome many of the technical problems, he founded the General Seafoods Company in Gloucester, Massachusetts. Birdseye's most important breakthrough came in 1927 when he developed a continuous-belt freezing process. By passing fresh fish through two moving belts sprayed with a freezing brine, he was able to achieve fast large-volume production of frozen foods. In 1929 Birdseye sold his patents and trademarks to what is now General Foods Corporation. In turn, that company broadened Birdseye's process to apply it to a whole range of food products and in 1930 introduced a line of frozen foods that included poultry, meat, fish, vegetables, and fruit in retail packages.

The initial reception of frozen foods was restricted greatly by a lack of freezer storage capacity, not only in the home, but of greater importance, in distribution networks. In 1933 only 516 stores in the United States were capable of handling frozen foods, but by 1940 between 12,000 and 15,000 stores boasted freezer cabinets. In 1940, 80 million pounds of frozen foods were sold through retail stores, while about 720 million pounds were sold to processors, bakers, and other institutional users.[9]

The outbreak of World War II brought new impetus to frozen foods. With canned products in short supply due to war requirements, the U.S. government encouraged the production of frozen foods for domestic use. During the war the number of freezers in stores doubled, and by 1945 the frozen food industry was swamped with orders from distributors for greater production. The prospect of enormous demand brought a flood of new packers into existence, many of whom were fly-by-night operators. In 1946 a mass of inferior quality frozen foods came to the market. The public rejected them overwhelmingly and the frozen

---

[9] Edward C. Hampe, Jr., and Merle Wittenberg, *The Lifeline of America* (New York, McGraw-Hill Book Company, 1964), p. 154.

foods industry, so recently optimistic, was left with an enormous surplus on its hands.

The earliest frozen vegetable products were common vegetable varieties, the original Birdseye line having included peas, corn, and spinach. By 1947, however, a wide range of vegetables were being sold, with the total retail pack (i.e., vegetables packed in small-sized containers) reaching 200 million pounds. By 1956 the total retail pack of vegetables reached 930 million pounds. Since 1956 sales of frozen vegetables have grown at a much slower rate. The retail pack of frozen vegetables in 1964 was 1,074 million pounds.

In the early 1960's a new form of frozen vegetable was introduced. Boil-in-bag vegetables, first marketed by Seabrook Farms Company, consisted of a frozen vegetable and butter (or other sauce) packed in a plastic pouch in which the product could be cooked. Although a boilable bag had been known to the industry for several years, it was the Green Giant Company which first aggressively promoted and marketed boil-in-bag vegetables. Introducing a line of seven vegetables in 1962 (the company's first entries in the frozen food field), Green Giant sold over $10 million of the frozen vegetables in its first year.[10] Other manufacturers followed suit. By 1965 nearly 48 million pounds in boil-in-bag vegetables were packed for retail sale in the United States.[11]

Between 1954 and 1964 sales of frozen vegetables at Grand Valley Markets almost doubled, while the number of items stocked increased from 33 to 107 (see Table 3-9). This increase reflected the *addition* of 109 items and the *dropping* of 43. Introduced by Grand Valley in 1964, boil-in-bag vegetables accounted for 15% of that year's volume. By 1964 new items introduced since 1954 accounted for almost 90% of the chain's frozen vegetable sales. Most of the new items, however, were new varieties introduced by established brands—only 23% of the 1964 volume was contributed by brands added since 1954.

---

[10] "Boilable Bag Breakthrough," *Quick Frozen Foods*, July 1963, p. 53.
[11] National Association of Frozen Food Packers, quoted in *Quick Frozen Foods*, June 1966, p. 75.

TABLE 3-9

GRAND VALLEY MARKETS

Frozen Vegetable Sales: 1954–1964

Year	Number of Items Stocked	Index of Sales Volume	% of Annual Sales Accounted for by:		
			New Items	New Brands	New Types
			(Introduced during preceding 2 years)		
1954	33	100	—	—	—
1956	N.A.	N.A.	N.A.	N.A.	N.A.
1958	33	134	77.3%*	3.9%*	0
1960	33	145	11.4	1.1	0
1962	68	160	32.0	15.1	0
1964	107	186	35.3	19.0	15.0%
			(Introduced since 1954)		
1964 vs. 1954			88.1%	23.0%	15.0%

* Because 1956 data were not available, figures for new items and brands in 1958 refer to items added in the *four*-year interval 1954–1958.

Liquid Dietary Foods

Faced with the knowledge that an estimated one out of five Americans were overweight, Mead Johnson and Company undertook in the 1950's to develop a new weight-reducing diet product which would provide an entire daily diet in the form of a tasty beverage. The result of the company's research was Metrecal, a dietary product introduced in powdered form in the fall of 1959 and shortly afterward in canned liquid form. There was no fanfare to the introduction; with no accompanying advertising, Metrecal was detailed to doctors and distributed at retail through drug stores only.

The company apparently failed to realize the size of the market it had touched upon. Metrecal was an instant success, the subject of widespread publicity, and was followed quickly by a host of imitators; Borden's Ready Diet, Pet Milk's Sego, Quaker Oats' Quota, and many others. By 1961 Americans consumed more than $110 million worth of liquid dietary foods.[12]

[12] "The Fat Market," *Sales Management*, April 1, 1966, pp. 47–50.

Shortly after 1961, however, the market assumed the proportions of a fad. Sales began to decline and by 1964 were at an annual level of $50 million. Of the major producers, only Mead Johnson and Pet Milk remained. By mid-1966 Metrecal and Sego were reportedly neck-and-neck, together sharing over 95% of the liquid dietary market. The market itself, after declining from its 1961 peak, had apparently passed through a fad phase and had grown by mid-1966 to an annual level of $70 million.

Sales data for liquid dietary foods at Grand Valley Markets were available for the year 1964 only. In that year liquid dietary product sales represented just under one-half of 1% of the chain's total grocery sales.

Margarine

A French scientist, Hippolyte Mege-Mouries, invented the product now known as margarine in response to a contest sponsored by Napoleon III for a palatable table fat. The product was patented in England in 1869 and by 1870, after the Franco-Prussian War, limited production was under way in France. In 1874 margarine was introduced to the United States.

The first margarines were manufactured primarily from animal fats (thus the term oleomargarine, "oleo" referring to animal fat), but in the early part of this century improved methods of refining vegetable oils gradually led to almost complete adoption of vegetable oils in lieu of the animal fats. Other improvements in ingredients and technology followed, including elimination of objectionable odors and flavors. The discovery of new processes in 1937 led to the use of soybean and cottonseed oils as the major fat ingredients, supplanting coconut oil. In 1941 standards of identity for margarine were established by the United States Food and Drug Administration.

In the late 1950's the now famous "heart" controversy struck the margarine industry. Briefly, medical research published at that time suggested a connection between certain kinds of food fat and cholesterol, a fatty-like substance which builds up in the arteries of the human body and is apparently related to disease. The food fats abetting cholesterol build-up were the saturated fats, such as predominate in butter. On the other hand, polyunsaturated fats, such as predominate in vegetable oils, tended to discourage cholesterol build-up in the body. Since margarine was made from vegetable oil, its raw material content was high in the desired polyunsaturated fats. In manufacture, however, existing types of margarine required a process called *hydrogenation* to give the product the stable shape characteristic of butter, and a result of this process was to give the final product an unfavorable ratio of saturated to polyunsaturated fats.

To produce a margarine high in polyunsaturates, and hence more desirable for heart health, margarine manufacturers turned to several new forms of the product. In 1958 Pitman-Moore Company brought out the first of the "health" margarines, Em Dee, which was not hydrogenated, hence had no shape, and was sold in cans. In 1959 Standard Brands became the first to market health margarines in food stores with two new products. The first was a hydrogenated corn oil margarine which the manufacturer claimed to be high in polyunsaturates, while the second was an unhydrogenated corn oil product which was frozen to give it shape. Corn oil margarines proved an almost instant success, and competitive brands followed quickly. In 1960 Corn Products' Mazola brand was introduced. Mazola, like many of the competitive brands which followed, was not pure corn oil, but rather consisted of unhydrogenated liquid corn oil added to other oils.

With polyunsaturates the basis of competitive claims, corn oil margarine quickly captured a substantial share of industry sales. By the end of 1963 it was estimated that corn oil accounted for 20% (by weight) of total margarine consumption.

Margarine consumption trends reflect the influence of changes in legislation, social conditions, and product innovation. The prewar period, with its burden of heavy legislative restriction, was one of low, stable margarine consumption. Per capita consumption of margarine and butter in 1925–1929 was 2.4 pounds and 17.9 pounds respectively, almost identical to the corresponding 1940 figures of 2.4 pounds and 17.0 pounds.[13] War conditions brought rise to increased margarine usage, however, and by 1945

---

[13] "Polyunsaturates Is Margarine Battle Cry," *Advertising Age*, September 4, 1961, p. 1.

per capita consumption had risen to 4.1 pounds. With the removal of restrictive legislation in the postwar period, margarine sales rapidly increased while those of butter concurrently declined. By 1957 per capita margarine consumption (at 8.6 pounds) exceeded that of butter (8.4 pounds) for the first time. The arrival of corn oil margarines in the late 1950's provided

Table 3-10

Grand Valley Markets

Margarine Sales: 1954–1964

Year	Number of Items Stocked	Index of Sales Volume	% of Annual Sales Accounted for by:		
			New Items	New Brands	New Types
			(Introduced during preceding 2 years)		
1954	9	100	—	—	—
1956	11	121	27.3%	18.4%	0
1958	13	130	11.7	7.5	0
1960	15	128	12.1	12.1	0
1962	25	141	39.9	17.4	26.5%
1964	20	147	4.6	3.9	0
			(Introduced since 1954)		
1964 vs. 1954			57.4%	41.9%	30.9%

added impetus to margarine growth, and by 1965 per capita consumption had risen to 9.9 pounds, as opposed to only 6.5 pounds for butter.

Margarine sales at the Grand Valley chain are shown in Table 3-10. By 1964 new items and brands introduced since 1954 accounted for 57.4% and 41.9% of sales respectively. The importance of corn oil products, first appearing in 1962, is substantial. By 1964 the corn oil margarines constituted over 30% of category sales.

In 1964 Anderson Clayton took product innovation in margarine a step further with the introduction of Chiffon, a soft margarine. Made primarily of safflower oil, the product was sold in plastic tubs and remained soft and spreadable even at refrigerator temperatures. By 1965 Chiffon had achieved national distribution and captured a 3% market share.[14] Imitators followed quickly among most national manufacturers, including Swift, whose Sundrop brand of soft margarine was marketed in a squeeze-type plastic bottle.

Nonfat Dry Milk

Powdered milk has been on the market since the early 1900's, but until World War II was used almost exclusively by large commercial bakeries, ice cream manufacturers, and other similar institutional users. In 1942 the Borden Company became the first to market a powdered milk product for home use when it introduced its Starlac brand of nonfat dry milk. The product was slow to gain acceptance at that time, at least in part due to prevailing aversion to dehydrated foods on the part of American servicemen. By the end of the war, however, consumers had begun to accept the idea of a powdered milk for home use and sales began to rise rapidly. Between 1950 and 1951 sales of powdered milk for home use increased from 17 million pounds to 60 million pounds.

Powdered milk is processed in exactly the same manner as ordinary milk, except that it is then dehydrated. Nonfat dry milk is, in essence, dehydrated skimmed milk, with only the fat and vitamin A removed from the original milk. The product's principal appeals are economy (less than one-third the cost of regular milk), convenience in storage, and the nutritional benefits of a skimmed milk.

For several years Borden dominated the consumer market for nonfat dry milk. In 1950, however, when sales began to climb rapidly, its first competitor on the national market, Land O'Lakes, emerged. By 1952 three nationally marketed brands (including Borden) competed with almost 50 regional brands for the dried milk market.[15] By 1953 the total home market for powdered milk had reached a reported 100 million pounds.[16]

[14] "Soft Margarines Toughen Ad Muscles in Test Areas as Sales Battle Looms," *Advertising Age*, February 14, 1966, p. 2.
[15] "Dried Milk: Consumers Like It," *Business Week*, September 27, 1952, p. 50.
[16] "New Lines Make Carnation More Contented," *Printers' Ink*, February 22, 1963, p. 108.

In 1954 Carnation Company introduced an improved version of the product possessing superior "instant" mixing qualities. Consumer research had suggested to Carnation that the public found existing brands of dry milk difficult to mix and not too desirable in taste, so the company had set out to develop an improved product. Carnation's own research efforts were not particularly successful, but in early 1954 its field staff discovered a small West Coast manufacturer test-marketing a vastly superior instant product. Carnation acquired the company and moved to market with the product under its own Carnation brand name.

Carnation sales rose rapidly, while competitors proved slow in improving their own products. It was not until 1958, for example, that the original leader, Borden, improved the formulation of its Starlac brand. By that time Carnation had gained market leadership with just over 30% share, while Borden had fallen to just under 30%.[17]

The mid-1950's saw also a "battle of big boxes" develop in the dried milk market. Early versions of the product had been marketed in 3-quart sizes, while average weekly milk consumption for a family at that time was about 8 quarts. In 1955 Borden introduced a 12-quart size, and Carnation quickly retaliated with an 8-quart package. Larger packages soon proved more acceptable to consumers, and many manufacturers dropped the earlier small packages altogether.

Nonfat dry milk sales at Grand Valley Markets are shown in Table 3-11. Most immediately apparent is the introduction of two new brands in 1956 (one of these was Carnation) which together comprised almost one-half of that year's sales. Although no additional new brands were added after 1956, new brands accounted for 64.5% of total sales in 1964. The importance of larger package sizes is reflected in the fact that by 1964 new items introduced since 1954 comprised almost 90% of the chain's sales in this category. After a period of substantial growth between 1954 and 1960, nonfat dry milk sales at Grand Valley have held fairly constant.

---

[17] *Ibid.*

TABLE 3-11

GRAND VALLEY MARKETS

Nonfat Dry Milk Sales: 1954–1964

Year	Number of Items Stocked	Index of Sales Volume	% of Annual Sales Accounted for by:		
			New Items	New Brands	New Types
			(Introduced during preceding 2 years)		
1954	4	100	—	—	—
1956	7	152	53.2%	45.3%	0
1958	9	190	31.4	0	0
1960	10	244	27.2	0	0
1962	9	239	23.1	0	0
1964	8	235	12.2	0	0
			(Introduced since 1954)		
1964 vs. 1954			87.4%	64.5%	0

Packaged Dessert Mixes

Some forms of prepared desserts have been on the market for well over a century. Dessert *mixes* (primarily puddings and flavored gelatins), however, did not achieve significance until the late 19th century. Rennet dessert mixes first appeared in 1878 when Charles Hansen's Laboratories, maker of Junket rennet dessert mix, was founded. The first brand of flavored gelatin dessert mix was Jell-O, introduced in 1897 by Genesee Pure Food Company of LeRoy, New York. Interestingly, the initial response to Jell-O was so poor that the company's owner once offered to sell the gelatin business for $35. There were no takers, so the product was recalled from the market for over a year while its formulation was improved. Royal, another well-known gelatin dessert, has been a product of Standard Brands since the company's formation in 1929.

During World War II consumer demand for packaged dessert mixes increased substantially. Rationing and shortages of packaged ice cream, sugar, and other ingredients diminished the availability of many other desserts, while a higher proportion of working women increased the demand for convenience food products. At the same time, however, shortages of ingredients at the manufacturers' level restricted supplies of dessert mixes. Some brands were dropped entirely, while others cut back on flavor varieties and/or distribution.

The postwar period saw the re-introduction of many of the flavors and varieties previously dropped. At the same time intense competition in this period brought about many new varieties of packaged dessert mixes. Most notable of these new additions was a range of varieties in a new class of dessert mix—instant puddings.

Instant puddings, requiring no cooking, were first introduced in 1948 by the American Maize Products Company. The first consumer product ever manufactured by the company, Amazo instant puddings were marketed in three flavors on a limited distribution basis. Other brands followed, but with some delay since Amazo's manufacturing process was patented and technical problems in developing a suitable instant pudding mix were considerable. For example, Royal and Jell-O, the brands which in later years came to dominate the instant pudding market, were introduced in 1952 and 1953, respectively.

In both gelatins and puddings and pie fillings, the most prevalent form of product innovation has been the introduction of new flavor varieties. Since 1954, for example, the major manufacturers of gelatin have added an average of almost one new flavor each year. Low calorie dessert mixes, first introduced in 1953, are also available in an increasing number of flavors.

The growth in flavor varieties is reflected in the stock of packaged dessert mixes maintained by Grand Valley Markets, as shown in Table 3-12. Between 1954 and 1964 the number of items stocked increased from 48 to 74, most of which was attributable to new flavor varieties (some of the flavored gelatins were also offered in larger package sizes). By 1964 new items introduced since 1954 accounted for almost one-half of that year's sales. Virtually all (99.2%) of the new items added were by previously existing brands. Only two new brands were added during the 10-year interval, and one of these (that introduced in 1956) was dropped in the following period. Total sales volume has grown only slightly since 1956.

TABLE 3-12

GRAND VALLEY MARKETS

Packaged Dessert Mix Sales: 1954–1964

Year	Number of Items Stocked	Index of Sales Volume	% of Annual Sales Accounted for by:		
			New Items	New Brands	New Types
			(Introduced during preceding 2 years)		
1954	48	100	—	—	—
1956	60	128	24.7%	3.3%	0
1958	51	133	6.5	0	0
1960	63	131	20.1	0	0
1962	68	131	13.8	0	0
1964	74	140	14.4	0.8	0
			(Introduced since 1954)		
1964 vs. 1954			49.1%	0.8%	0

In the total United States market, sales of packaged dessert mixes have risen from $87 million in 1951 to a 1964 high of over $162 million. Inflation of food prices and increases in population, however, account for most of the increase. In fact, on a unit-per-capita basis, 1964 consumption of packaged desserts was almost identical with that of 1954.

Packaged Rice

Rice culture began before man's ability to write and keep records; its origins are consequently not clear. An ancient Chinese manuscript provides the first recorded mention of rice around 2800 B.C. The advent of a rice industry in the United States seems to have occurred in 1685 when a British sailing ship carrying rice was forced to land in Charleston, South Carolina, for repairs. A small thriving rice industry soon developed in the area of the Carolinas, but later declined as western areas of the United States proved more suitable for rice growing.

For many years the domestic rice market was characterized by a relatively low, stable consumption concentrated in a few areas and influenced by certain ethnic groups. As late as 1940 rice was still shipped only in 100 pound bags and sold at retail in bulk. Packaging of rice in consumer-sized units did not begin until the later stages of World War II, but since that time rice has shown substantial growth in consumer usage.

Packaged rice is available in a number of different processed forms. *Regular milled* rice is uncooked and may be of the common white type or the lesser-used brown type. *Parboiled* rice is treated by a special steam pressure process before milling—the treatment aids in retention of much of the natural mineral and vitamin content of rice, but the product requires longer cooking time than regular rice. Various processes for parboiling have been patented, but most are said to be variants of a very ancient process employed in some areas of India, Burma, and Ceylon. *Precooked* packaged rice is probably the newest type of the product and, at least in some forms, is a uniquely American innovation. After precooking the rice is dehydrated. Rice in this form requires only very brief cooking by the user.

Precooked rice began with the introduction of General Foods' Minute Rice in 1946—the idea for the product had actually come to General Foods from an outside source. In 1941 a gentleman who introduced himself as Ataullah K. Ozai Durrani, cousin of the King of Afghanistan, demonstrated a crude precooked rice of his own invention to the company. Working with Durrani, General Foods set out to perfect a precooked rice which would require partial cooking by the consumer. By 1942 an experimental pilot plant had been completed, but at this stage the U.S. Army approached the company with the object of securing the product for field ration use. Further, the Army requested an end product requiring no cooking at all. General Foods met the Army's request and continued to supply precooked rice throughout the war.

In 1946 Minute Rice was introduced to the civilian market on a test-market basis. The product proved immensely popular, and sales were subsequently expanded to other areas. Because precooking technology was difficult and the General Foods process was protected by patent, other manufacturers could not follow quickly. By the early 1950's other precooked packaged rice products were available on the market—most, however, were of the "quick-cooking" type, requiring some partial cooking by the user before serving. More recently, in the early 1960's, precooked packaged rices have also become increasingly popular in the form of specialty rice products—that is, packaged rice mixed with other ingredients to form a dish or a meal.

In 1946 per capita consumption of rice in the United States was 4.7 pounds. During the postwar period rice consumption

TABLE 3-13

GRAND VALLEY MARKETS

Packaged Rice Sales: 1954–1964

Year	Number of Items Stocked	Index of Sales Volume	% of Annual Sales Accounted for by:		
			New Items	New Brands	New Types
			(Introduced during preceding 2 years)		
1954	6	100	—	—	—
1956	8	116	2.7%	1.0%	0
1958	9	124	17.8	4.8	0
1960	9	133	0	0	0
1962	10	149	15.8	0	0
1964	20	173	37.5	20.3	19.7%
			(Introduced since 1954)		
1964 vs. 1954			54.0%	20.3%	19.7%

has steadily grown because of increased convenience (in the form of packaging and product preparation time) and the availability of rice in new varieties of dishes and meals. Per capita consumption in 1955 was 5.8 pounds; in 1960, 6.2 pounds; and in 1964, 7.6 pounds.[18]

The contribution of the specialty rice products to an increase in rice consumption is reflected in the experience of Grand Valley Markets, shown in Table 3-13. Until 1962 packaged rice sales at the chain had shown steady, but not dramatic, growth. The

---

[18] U.S. Department of Agriculture, *The Rice Situation*, December 1957, p. 8, and January 1966, p. 13.

addition of specialty products in 1964, however, resulted in a substantial upsurge in sales. In 1964 specialty products contributed almost 20% of the sales volume and were largely responsible for a doubling of the number of stocked items between 1962 and 1964. New brands of rice, which until 1964 had been of negligible importance, now contributed 20% of sales. By 1964 items which had been introduced since 1954 accounted for 54% of Grand Valley's sales of packaged rice products.

Peanut Butter

Peanut butter is a uniquely American product, manufactured and consumed only in the United States and Canada. Europeans not only do not like it, but they flatly refuse to eat it. At one point, peanut butter was offered to French and German families on the brink of starvation, but they allegedly preferred to go hungry rather than eat the "horrible tasting mixture that sticks to the roof of the mouth." [19]

Peanut butter first appeared in this country in 1890 when a physician in a St. Louis sanitarium prescribed it for some of his patients as a nutritious, easily digested food, high in proteins and low in carbohydrates. Patients apparently liked the product for, after returning home, many asked if they could buy it by mail. Soon afterwards, peanut butter was being marketed commercially by a number of small producers, most using meat grinders and coffee mills to grind the nuts. Sold by the pound from an open tub, early peanut butter was "chunky" and subject to oil separation and short shelf life.

Since those early days many new developments have served to improve peanut butter quality. Oil stabilizers prevent separation, and consistency and flavor have been vastly improved. Processing and packaging methods are also better. No radically new form of the product, however, has appeared on the market in many years.

In recent years the price of peanut butter has shown a slight decline; between 1956 and 1964, for example, average retail price

---

[19] *New York Times*, August 28, 1950.

declined about 5%. This price reduction, coupled with an increased proportion of school-aged children in the population (families with school-aged children tend to use more peanut butter) [20] has apparently contributed to a unit-per-capita increase in peanut butter consumption. In 1964 total retail sales of peanut butter

TABLE 3-14

GRAND VALLEY MARKETS

Peanut Butter Sales: 1954–1964

Year	Number of Items Stocked	Index of Sales Volume	% of Annual Sales Accounted for by:		
			New Items	New Brands	New Types
			(Introduced during preceding 2 years)		
1954	7	100	—	—	—
1956	11	122	9.9%	8.2%	0
1958	10	126	11.0	11.0	0
1960	11	137	14.3	0	0
1962	15	149	25.5	5.6	0
1964	17	158	12.2	10.7	0
			(Introduced since 1954)		
1964 vs. 1954			45.8%	21.1%	0

in the United States were $175 million, compared with only $121 million just eight years previously.

Table 3-14 shows peanut butter sales at the Grand Valley Markets chain. Between 1954 and 1964 total volume increased by almost 60%. The substantial growth in items stocked (from 7 to 17) is attributable in part to the addition of new brands but also to a prevailing trend toward larger container sizes. Most manufacturers added larger containers to their peanut butter lines during this period. New brands introduced since 1954 accounted for 21% of 1964 sales, while new items comprised almost 46% of the 1964 volume.

[20] U.S. Department of Agriculture, *Homemakers' Use and Opinions About Peanuts*, Marketing Research Report No. 203, November 1957.

Pet Foods

The pet food industry had its beginning in 1855, when a small British manufacturer (Spratt's) started making leftover sailors' hardtack into pet food. Dry pet foods (biscuits or cereal) remained as the only prepared product until about 1925 when Chappel Brothers, Illinois horse dealers, introduced a canned horsemeat dog food. Other canned pet food brands, primarily beef, horse, or fish based, followed quickly. Canned foods soon came to dominate the market and by the advent of World War II accounted for a majority of all pet food sales.

The war, however, brought a shortage of both tin cans and meat, and many pet owners were forced to switch to the dry foods or to revert to table scraps for their pets. When the war ended, a big upsurge in pet food sales began, and it was in the dry segment that the bulk of the growth occurred.

In 1956 a major innovation was introduced in the dry food segment, when the Ralston Purina Company introduced Dog Chow, an extruded, puffed-up dry dog food said to be more palatable than existing pellet or meal products. Almost immediately, Dog Chow achieved market leadership in the dry segment. General Foods soon retaliated with its own extruded product, Gaines Gravy Train, which also met with widespread acceptance. New dry dog food brands in a variety of forms, varieties, and flavors have since entered the market, while older types have fallen off considerably in market share. Dry *cat* food, meanwhile, was largely overlooked until the early 1960's when a host of new products stimulated sales to such an extent that, in 1964, dry cat food was the fastest growing segment of the entire pet food industry.

In 1963 yet another major innovation spurred the market with the introduction of Gainesburgers, a semimoist dog food, by the General Foods Corporation. A meat product with 50% of its water removed, the semimoist product resembled hamburger patties. It possessed the nutritive content of a one-pound can of dog food but required less storage space and no refrigeration. In just over a year Gainesburgers was outselling all but the leading brand of canned dog food. By early 1966 every major manufacturer of dog food reportedly had introduced or was developing a semi-moist product.

Table 3-15 illustrates the importance of new pet food products to the Grand Valley chain. By 1964 sales in the category had steadily increased to over twice their 1954 level; the number of items stocked had concurrently grown almost fourfold. New items introduced in the entire 10-year interval accounted for

TABLE 3-15

GRAND VALLEY MARKETS

Pet Food Sales: 1954–1964

Year	Number of Items Stocked	Index of Sales Volume	% of Annual Sales Accounted for by:		
			New Items	New Brands	New Types
			(Introduced during preceding 2 years)		
1954	23	100	—	—	—
1956	42	122	29.5%	18.1%	0
1958	47	178	16.8	4.7	0
1960	58	191	15.5	7.9	0
1962	74	211	23.9	2.0	0
1964	84	239	20.4	7.7	4.0%
			(Introduced since 1954)		
1964 vs. 1954			65.3%	44.4%	4.0%

almost two-thirds of the 1964 volume, while new brands accounted for 44% of 1964 sales. Particularly noticeable are the figures for 1956, when a substantial number of new items and new brands accounted respectively for 29.5% and 18.1% of that year's volume. In this case most of the new commodities were dry dog foods, reflecting both the over-all trend to this segment and the intro-duction of extruded products. In 1964 semimoist dog foods com-prised 4% of total category sales.

Powdered Coffee Creamers

In 1952 the Columbus, Ohio, firm of M & R Dietetic Labora-tories introduced an entirely new kind of dairy product—a powdered instant cream for lightening coffee. Storable without refrigeration and convenient to use in small quantities, the product seemed to be a natural complement to the rapidly expanding soluble coffee market.

Pream, however, did not really "take off" in the manner some had expected. For almost a decade, the product was the only one of its kind on the market, and sales levels remained relatively low. Consumers, apparently, just did not like the product —a fact later confirmed by marketing research studies.

In 1962 a new brand of powdered coffee creamer entered the market. Unlike Pream, which was a dairy product, Carnation's Coffee Mate was a synthetic made with a vegetable oil base. Backed by an extensive television advertising campaign, Coffee Mate was almost an instant success. Within its first year the synthetic product had captured market leadership. Other manufacturers soon entered the market with synthetic products, notably Pet Milk's Please, Borden's Cremora, and some chain-owned private brands. From total sales of $10.5 million in 1962 sales more than trebled to a 1964 level of $32.4 million. The Carnation product, however, continued to hold a lion's share of that market—reportedly over 80% in mid-1965.[21] Faced with the erosion of a market it had once held entirely, Pream finally abandoned its dairy-based formulation in 1964 in favor of an entirely new synthetic composition.

Between 1954 and 1960 the original dairy-based Pream brand was the only powdered coffee creamer carried by the Grand Valley chain, as shown in Table 3-16. During this period sales volume showed no substantial increase, although the addition of a larger container size to the line in 1960 accounted for nearly 70% of the year's sales. The addition of Carnation's synthetic creamer in 1962, however, and of similar products by Pet Milk and Borden in 1964, rapidly stimulated sales. By 1964 volume was six times the 1954 level and Grand Valley had dropped the original Pream brand entirely—the new synthetics accounted for 100% of powdered coffee creamer sales in 1964.

---

[21] "Happy Ending for a Product That Flopped," *Printers' Ink*, April 23, 1964, p. 29.

TABLE 3-16

GRAND VALLEY MARKETS

Powdered Coffee Creamer Sales: 1954–1964

Year	Number of Items Stocked	Index of Sales Volume	% of Annual Sales Accounted for by:		
			New Items	New Brands	New Types
			(Introduced during preceding 2 years)		
1954	1	100	—	—	—
1956	1	61	0	0	0
1958	1	93	0	0	0
1960	2	113	69.8%	0	0
1962	3	243	69.0	69.0%	69.0%
1964	5	599	69.9	14.6	0
			(Introduced since 1954)		
1964 vs. 1954			100%	100%	100%

Salad Dressings [22]

Salad dressings have been in use in the United States for many years. Since the 1920's consumption of these products has shown a steady increase. In 1922 per capita consumption of salad dressings was less than a pint; in 1939, 2.5 pints; in 1947, 4.4 pints; and by 1964, 7.0 pints. The steady growth seems in large part attributable to increased salad consumption, greater use of dressings and condiments in the home, and a tendency away from the use of home-prepared dressings. Total United States production in 1964 was 167.8 million gallons.

Salad dressings are generally classified into two groups of products: nonpourable (or spoonable) and pourable. As implied by the classification, the nonpourables are thick, semisolid substances, while the pourables are liquid in composition.

[22] Within the context of this summary the term "salad dressing" is used in a broad sense to include *all* products generally used to flavor salads, *including* mayonnaise. For clarity, the *specific product* defined by the Food and Drug Administration as salad dressing is referred to here as nonpourable *white salad dressing.*

Mayonnaise and white salad dressing are the two major types of nonpourable dressings. Both are manufactured in this country under standards established by the U.S. Food and Drug Administration in 1950 and consist of edible vegetable oil, vinegar or lemon juice, and various spices or flavorings. Eggs are also added to act as emulsifiers to enable the oil and vinegar to mix. Mayonnaise, however, contains a high proportion of oil, while white salad dressing contains starch and water in lieu of a high oil content.

Nonpourable dressings, which constitute over 80% of all salad dressing production, have remained virtually unchanged in form for many years. Within the nonpourable group of products, mayonnaise has shown the most rapid growth: [23] in 1946 mayonnaise accounted for 35.2% of all dressings produced, while in 1964 its share had grown to 42.0%. During the same period white nonpourable salad dressings declined from a 53.9% share to 37.9%. Highly substitutable products, the relative consumption of mayonnaise and white salad dressing appears closely linked to the fortunes of consumer disposable income. During the prosperous postwar period consumers have showed a preference for the higher-quality, higher-priced mayonnaise. During the depression, however, the trend in consumption was the reverse, with white salad dressing gaining considerably at the expense of mayonnaise.

Sales of nonpourable dressings at Grand Valley Markets are shown in Table 3-17. Total chain sales in 1964 were approximately 50% greater than the 1954 level. The extent of new product activity in the category has been extremely small, with over 80% of the 1964 volume being accounted for by brands and items that had been carried by Grand Valley for at least 10 years.

Pourable dressings are usually mixtures of oil, vinegar, and various spices or flavorings. Since World War II pourable dressings have shown the most rapid growth of all segments of the salad dressing market. Total commercial production of pourable dressings in the United States has grown from 3.6 million gallons in 1946 to 21.7 million gallons in 1964; the pourables' share of

---

[23] Unless otherwise specified, the data in this section are based on statistics drawn from various annual editions of the U.S. Department of Commerce publication, *Salad Dressing, Mayonnaise and Related Products.*

all salad dressing sales has increased from 6.2% to 12.9% in the
same period. Contributing to this growth has been the host of
new flavors and varieties of pourable dressings introduced in recent
years. Low-calorie dietetic dressings have also contributed to the
greater selection.

The introduction of *dry* salad dressing mixes (to which the
housewife adds her own oil and vinegar) has also aided the increased popularity of pourable dressings. First created in the late

TABLE 3-17

GRAND VALLEY MARKETS

Nonpourable Salad Dressing Sales: 1954–1964

Year	Number of Items Stocked	Index of Sales Volume	% of Annual Sales Accounted for by:		
			New Items	New Brands	New Types
			(Introduced during preceding 2 years)		
1954	15	100	—	—	—
1956	15	151	0	0	0
1958	18	151	13.3%	13.3%	0
1960	18	156	0	0	0
1962	21	151	12.3	12.3	0
1964	19	156	8.2	6.0	0
			(Introduced since 1954)		
1964 vs. 1954			18.6%	16.4%	0

1940's by a restaurant chef, dry mixes were initially marketed
through gift shops and specialty stores under the brand name
Four Seasons. In 1954 the brand was acquired by General Foods
Corporation, which in turn expanded the line of flavors, changing
the brand name to Good Seasons. By 1964 dry salad dressing
mixes accounted for over 13% of retail pourable volume.

The extent of product innovation in pourable dressings is
indicated by the statistics from Grand Valley Markets, as shown
in Table 3-18. During the period 1954 to 1964 sales have increased
over fivefold. The number of items stocked has grown from only
5 items in 1954 to 46 in 1964 (the increase was made up of 77

items added, 36 dropped during the 10-year interval). In almost every year new items comprised about one-third of total sales, and, in 1956 almost two-thirds of the year's sales. By 1964 new items introduced in the previous 10 years accounted for over 90% of total sales. New brands introduced in the same 10-year interval accounted for over 60% of total volume. Dry salad dressing mixes, first carried in 1956, comprised 9.1% of Grand Valley's pourable dressing sales in 1964.

TABLE 3-18

GRAND VALLEY MARKETS

Pourable Salad Dressing Sales: 1954–1964

Year	Number of Items Stocked	Index of Sales Volume	% of Annual Sales Accounted for by:		
			New Items	New Brands	New Types
			(Introduced during preceding 2 years)		
1954	5	100	—	—	—
1956	23	268	63.5%	43.6%	6.8%
1958	38	330	36.3	8.7	0
1960	45	413	25.3	3.4	0
1962	51	549	33.1	11.5	0
1964	46	567	32.4	0	0
			(Introduced since 1954)		
1964 vs. 1954			90.3%	60.4%	9.1%

Soluble (Instant) Coffee

A bar of soluble coffee, to be eaten or immersed in boiling water, was known during the American Civil War. Other soluble coffees were patented as early as the beginning of the 19th century, primarily in Europe. An American chemist, G. Washington, invented a soluble coffee which was placed on the United States market under the brand name G. Washington in 1909. Despite its early existence, however, soluble coffee was virtually unknown to most Americans prior to World War II; in 1941 considerably less than 1% of all coffee consumed in the United States was of the soluble type.[24]

During World War II, however, the Armed Forces used soluble coffee extensively, and millions of American servicemen tasted it for the first time. In the words of one manufacturer, this "was the finest sampling job for the product ever done." [25] By 1946 there were approximately 30 brands of soluble coffee on the market, compared with only a handful in the prewar period.[26] Rapid growth of the market soon followed. By 1951 soluble coffee accounted for over 5% of all coffee consumed; the figure grew to 12.7% in 1954, 18.4% in 1958, and eventually reached an apparent ceiling of about 21% in the early 1960's. Total United States consumption of soluble coffee in 1951 was 227 million units (2-ounce equivalent); in 1960, 1,098 million units; and in 1964, 1,159 million units.[27]

Most of the early brands of soluble coffee were of the so-called café type, in which various carbohydrates were added to hold the coffee flavor. Nescafé, the early leader in the field, was of this type. Gradually, however, the "pure" type of soluble coffee (to which no carbohydrates are added) came to prevail, apparently because consumers did not like the sweetness implied by the addition of carbohydrates. By 1956 all major manufacturers had switched to pure soluble coffee, and the café type had virtually disappeared.

As shown in Table 3-19, the sales of soluble coffee by the Grand Valley chain since 1954 reflect a relatively low level of new product activity. The number of items stocked by Grand Valley remained relatively stable throughout the period, and new brands introduced since 1954 accounted for only 11.2% of 1964 volume. While new items introduced since 1954 comprised about one-third of the 1964 sales, most of the new items were larger container sizes.

---

[24] "Soluble Coffee—Not the Best Breakfast Beverage," *Consumers Research Bulletin*, December 1945, p. 19.

[25] "Overcoming Resistance to New Type of Product," *Printers' Ink*, March 29, 1946, p. 25.

[26] *Ibid.*, p. 24.

[27] Pan American Coffee Bureau, *Annual Coffee Statistics*, 1964.

Between 1954 and 1964 the index of sales volume for instant coffee declined by about a third. This decline reflects a very substantial reduction in average retail prices; according to the Pan American Coffee Bureau, the U.S. average price of a 2-oz. package of instant coffee fell from 60.6 cents in 1954 to 33.0 cents in 1964, a decline of 46%. If the average price of instant coffee at Grand

TABLE 3-19

GRAND VALLEY MARKETS

Soluble Coffee Sales: 1954–1964

Year	Number of Items Stocked	Index of Sales Volume	% of Annual Sales Accounted for by:		
			New Items	New Brands	New Types
			(*Introduced during preceding 2 years*)		
1954	19	100	—	—	—
1956	21	120	13.0%	3.3%	0
1958	21	101	14.6	14.1	0
1960	20	89	15.7	10.1	0
1962	24	85	35.4	3.3	0
1964	18	67	5.2	0	0
			(*Introduced since 1954*)		
1964 vs. 1954			33.6%	11.2	0

Valley Markets declined by a similar proportion, then an index of *physical* volume for 1964 would be approximately 124 (1954 = 100).

In 1964, with consumption of soluble coffee actually declining on a per capita basis, General Foods Corporation began test-marketing the first new form of the product to reach the market in many years. Maxim is a freeze-dried soluble coffee which is said to approximate the flavor and aroma of freshly percolated coffee more closely. By 1966 Maxim had moved into additional test markets, but its eventual impact on the soluble coffee market was yet to be determined.

Vegetable Shortening and Cooking Oil

Fats and oils, representing a major source of dietary needs, have always played an important part in man's food requirements. Until the latter half of the 19th century, most of these requirements were met by the natural fat content of many foods, plus a few commodities such as lard, butter, and olive oil.

Cooking (and salad) oils are prepared from vegetable oils that are usually refined, bleached, and deodorized. As early as 600 b.c. the Greeks produced and commercially marketed olive oil. While olive oil enjoyed considerable popularity in Europe for many centuries, the principal edible oil products in the United States for many years were lard and other animal fats. Vegetable oils were almost unheard of here until late in the 19th century. At that time large amounts of cottonseed oil became available as a by-product of the growing of cotton, but early attempts to market cottonseed oil products failed due to an unpleasant odor associated with the oil. Then, in 1899 Wesson invented a process of deodorizing cottonseed and other vegetable oils by forcing steam through the oils under a vacuum. With that invention the production of an acceptable liquid cooking oil became possible.

Shortenings (so called because they impart a tender or "short" quality to baked goods) are fats used in the preparation of many foods. Early shortenings called "compound" shortenings were made in the late 19th century by blending liquid cottonseed oil with animal fats to give a semisolid product. Just three years after Wesson's deodorizing invention, however, the French invented the process of *hydrogenation* which made possible the pure vegetable oil shortenings which we know today. Briefly, hydrogenation involves the addition of hydrogen to liquid oils to convert them to a semisolid state. From this point on hydrogenated vegetable shortenings became increasingly popular while lard was used less and less. Many types of vegetable oil can be used in shortening products—cottonseed oil was the primary source for early versions, but in more recent times soybean oil has been the most important source.

Many of the brands of cooking oil and shortening on the market in the 1960's have been available for many years, although improvements and changes in product formulation occurred in that time. In the late 1950's, for example, the "heart scare" (see section on margarine) brought many manufacturers to increase the poly-unsaturate content in their cooking oil and shortening products. Crisco cooking oil, introduced by Procter and Gamble in the early 1960's, employed new processing techniques for soybean oil which resulted in a clear white oil, promoted as the first "non-oily" product in its product class. By 1964 sales of Crisco exceeded all but the two long-entrenched leaders in the field, Wesson and Mazola.

In 1964 United States retail sales of shortening products totaled over $170 million. In the postwar period since 1947 unit-per-capita sales have held almost constant. Retail sales of cooking oil, however, have shown remarkable growth during the same period. In 1950 retail sales of cooking oil totaled $42.4 million, while in 1964 over $156 million of cooking oil products were sold at retail. Since the average price of cooking oil actually declined during this period, the increase in unit sales has been even greater. The reason for such growth is not altogether clear, although it appears to be related to a general upgrading of edible oils used in the

TABLE 3-20

GRAND VALLEY MARKETS

Vegetable Shortening Sales: 1956–1964

Year	Number of Items Stocked	Index of Sales Volume	% of Annual Sales Accounted for by:		
			New Items	New Brands	New Types
			(Introduced during preceding 2 years)		
1954	N.A.	N.A.	N.A.	N.A.	N.A.
1956	5	100	—	—	—
1958	7	155	23.8%	23.8%	0
1960	8	156	0.5	0.5	0
1962	8	156	11.9	11.9	0
1964	6	157	0	0	0
			(Introduced since 1956)		
1964 vs. 1956			51.2%	51.2%	0

home—in simplified terms, a substitution of shortening for lard and of cooking oil for both shortening and lard.

Vegetable shortening sales at Grand Valley Markets are shown in Table 3-20. After a substantial growth in 1956–1958 volume has remained relatively stable, while the number of items stocked by the chain has also held constant. The high proportion of 1964 volume attributable to new brands and items introduced since

TABLE 3-21

GRAND VALLEY MARKETS

Cooking Oil Sales: 1954–1964

Year	Number of Items Stocked	Index of Sales Volume	% of Annual Sales Accounted for by:		
			New Items	New Brands	New Types
			(Introduced during preceding 2 years)		
1954	7	100	—	—	—
1956	9	150	8.8%	8.8%	0
1958	13	275	31.0	31.0	0
1960	19	321	40.8	14.6	0
1962	22	366	26.1	21.8	0
1964	25	388	12.2	0.7	0
			(Introduced since 1954)		
1964 vs. 1954			78.6%	46.0%	0

1956 is primarily attributable to the growing success of a chain-owned brand of shortening. First introduced in 1962, the private brand was by 1964 outselling all other brands of shortening stocked by the Grand Valley chain.

In contrast to the vegetable shortening case, Grand Valley's sales of cooking oil are illustrated in Table 3-21. The 1964 volume of cooking oil is almost four times that of 1954, while the addition of new brands and larger container sizes has resulted in a similar, nearly fourfold increase in the number of items stocked. Grand Valley added at least one new brand in each period, and by 1964 brands introduced since 1954 accounted for 46% of sales. New items added during the same 10-year period accounted for 78.6% of 1964 volume.

Summary

Processed foods in the United States have undergone substantial change in the period since World War II. Among the product categories selected for examination in this study, for example:

- Seven categories (dehydrated potatoes, frozen dinners and specialties, frozen juice concentrates, liquid dietary foods, nonfat dry milk, packaged rice, and powdered coffee creamers) were introduced to the consumer market for the first time at some point during or since World War II.
- Three other categories (cake mixes, frozen vegetables, and instant coffee) were introduced in the period preceding World War II, but held a position of almost negligible sales volume prior to the war. The growth of these processed foods to a place of prominence in food consumption occurred almost entirely in the period during and since the war.

√While entirely new categories are certainly one reflection of product innovation, it is also true that substantial changes in product have occurred within the categories as well. *New types* of product have been introduced in the following categories since World War II:

- Cold breakfast cereals: Presweetened (1949) and nutritional (1955) cereals, which together have accounted for the entire increase in per capita consumption of cold cereal products.
- Dehydrated potatoes: Specialty products introduced in the late 1950's.
- Flour: Instant-blending flour (1963), an example of one attempt to stay or reverse a declining trend in per capita consumption of a processed food category.
- Frozen juice concentrates: Synthetic juices (1963), containing no natural fruit content but offering a sweeter tasting product and not subject to unexpected changes in raw material supply.
- Frozen vegetables: Boil-in-the-bag vegetables (early 1960's) with butter or other sauces sealed in a plastic pouch in which the product is cooked.
- Margarine: Corn oil margarines (1959) offering a high ratio of polyunsaturated fats to reduce the danger of heart disease; soft margarines (1964), which can be spread easily at refrigerator temperatures.

TABLE 3-22

GRAND VALLEY MARKETS

Comparison of Product Category Growth Rates and Extent of Product Innovation: 1954–1964

Product Category	Sales Volume Index (1954 = 100)	% of 1964 Sales Accounted for by:		
		New Items Introduced since 1954	New Brands Introduced since 1954	New Types Introduced since 1954
HIGH GROWTH CATEGORIES (Sales Volume Index 200 or Higher)				
Dehydrated Potatoes	1,804	83.4%	59.6%	46.7%
Powdered Coffee Creamers	599	100.0	100.0	100.0
Pourable Salad Dressing	567	90.3	60.4	9.1
Frozen Dinners and Specialties	483	87.7	54.6	N.A.
Cooking Oil	388	78.1	46.0	0
Pet Foods	239	65.3	44.0	4.0
Nonfat Dry Milk	235	87.4	64.5	0
Cold Breakfast Cereal	231	67.8	6.2	13.4
Weighted Averages: All High Growth Categories	354	75.3%	40.8%	7.9%

LOW GROWTH CATEGORIES
(*Sales Volume Index Less Than 140*)*

Soluble Coffee	67	33.6%	0
Evaporated and Condensed Milk	68	26.8	0
Hot Breakfast Cereal	93	18.5	0
All-Purpose Flour	131	34.3	10.7%
Weighted Averages: All Low Growth Categories	80	30.7%	1.8%

* Although frozen juice concentrates had a 1964 Sales Volume Index of 131, this category was not classified as low growth. The 1964 index reflected the effects of the December 1962 Florida orange crop freeze and was apparently atypical in comparison with the trend in that category for preceding years.

SOURCE: Warehouse withdrawal records, Grand Valley Markets.

- Packaged rice: Specialty precooked rice products, introduced in the late 1950's.
- Pet foods: Semimoist products, first introduced in this country in 1963 and by early 1966 reported to be marketed or under development by every major pet food manufacturer in the country.
- Powdered coffee creamers: Synthetic, nondairy creamers (1962), which very quickly almost entirely displaced the earlier dairy-based product formulations.
- Pourable salad dressings: Dry salad dressing mixes, first introduced to food stores in 1954 and growing to account for over 10% of a rapidly expanding product category.

The new types of products described above appear to have established their position in the market firmly and to have become regular fixtures in the food consumption patterns of Americans. In early 1966, however, the food industry was carefully observing the progress of other new types of products recently introduced. Cold cereals containing freeze-dried fruit, instant hot cereals, and freeze-dried soluble coffee, for example, were all viewed with cautious optimism, but the success of such products remains yet to be determined. Within every category studied in the analysis of the chain shipments records, at least some *new brands* and *new items* were introduced during the period 1954–1964.

Product Innovation and Rates of Growth

While the postwar period has seen many and different forms of product innovation, it is also apparent that innovative activities have not been uniformly distributed among all product categories. The analysis of the chain warehouse shipments data indicate that there is a *relationship* between product innovation and category growth. Table 3-22 compares two groups of categories, those experiencing high and low growth during the period 1964, in terms of the extent of product innovation in each group. Among categories whose sales volume more than doubled, new items introduced since 1954 accounted for an average 75.3% of sales. On the other hand, among categories whose sales volume either declined or increased by less than 40%, comparable new items accounted for only 30.7% of sales. Similarly, new brands and new types of products accounted for a substantially higher proportion of sales among the high growth categories than among the low growth group.

Obviously, there is a distinct relationship between product innovation and category growth, but there is also no simple manner of determining the direction of causality here. On one hand, a rapidly growing category will most certainly attract new items and new brands. At the same time, however, it is also probable that at least some of the innovative products so attracted would contribute to further category growth that would not have occurred in their absence. It seems probable that both phenomena have been at work during the 1950's and 1960's.

Extent of Product Innovation

From analysis of the 21 product categories for which chain shipment records were available, some estimates of the overall extent of product innovation during the period 1954–1964 can be derived. Combined estimates of sales volume for new items, new brands, and new types of food products are presented in Table 3-23.

In each year the percentage of sales accounted for by *new items* is approximately 20% to 25%. This figure has been virtually stable in recent years. On the whole, there has apparently been no overall increase in the share of processed food sales accounted for by new items that were added by the chain. *New brands*, in fact, have found it increasingly difficult to gain acceptance; the share of sales volume accounted for by new brands has declined in each successive period since 1954. *New types* of products, representing a higher order of product innovation, have shown a considerable increase. In 1956 new types accounted for only 0.9% of total sales; by 1964 the comparable figure was 2.5% of total volume.

If the Grand Valley Markets experience can be considered as representative of typical retail food store trends in the United States, the results can be projected to give an indication of the extent of product innovation, and its importance, in the total market for processed foods. In 1964 total U.S. retail sales of processed foods (excluding meat, dairy, produce, and fresh baked goods) were estimated to be $16.0 billion.[28] If new items, new brands, and

[28] *Food Topics*, September 1965.

TABLE 3-23

GRAND VALLEY MARKETS

Sales Volume of New Items, New Brands, and New Types of Products, 21-Category Totals: 1956–1964

Year	New Items Sales Volume of Items Introduced since Preceding Period		New Brands Sales Volume of Brands Introduced since Preceding Period		New Types Sales Volume of Types of Products Introduced since Preceding Period	
	Dollars*	% of Total Annual Sales	Dollars*	% of Total Annual Sales	Dollars*	% of Total Annual Sales
1956	$784,269	26.6%	$373,913	12.7%	$ 26,945	0.9%
1958	808,461	24.0	437,688	13.0	0	0
1960	694,438	20.5	357,007	10.6	8,128	0.2
1962	776,922	22.9	254,351	7.5	56,958	1.7
1964	756,871	21.8	204,124	5.9	88,313	2.5
1964 vs. 1954†	$2,244,444	64.7%	$1,072,577	30.9%	$246,723	7.1%

* Dollar volumes adjusted for Grand Valley growth, as explained in Chapter 1.
† Refers to all new items, brands, and types introduced *since 1954*.

SOURCE: Warehouse withdrawal records, Grand Valley Markets.

new types of products represented the same proportions of this total as they did in the 1964 sales of Grand Valley Markets, then total national retail sales of these groups of products may be estimated as follows:

	Sales in 1964 of Products:	
	Introduced since 1962	*Introduced since 1954*
New Items	$3,501,000,000	$10,393,000,000
New Brands	947,000,000	4,900,000,000
New Types	401,000,000	1,157,000,000

CHAPTER 4

New Product Research and Development

NEW FOOD PRODUCTS are the visible results of the process of innovation in food processing. During the 1950's and 1960's the principal source of such innovation has been the research and development (R&D) activities of large food processing companies. Large private companies are not, of course, the sole originators of new products; many of the products discussed in the preceding chapter were developed wholly or in part by individual inventors, small companies, and government agencies. Nevertheless, as is shown in the first part of this chapter, formalized R&D by large firms has gradually become the most important single source of new products. In the remainder of the chapter, we devote our attention to the nature of food processors' R&D activities. Information is presented on the major steps involved in developing and testing new products prior to their introduction and on the costs and time requirements for carrying out these steps. This information was obtained through a survey of food processing companies, as explained in Chapter 1.

The Changing Sources of Product Innovation

In Chapter 3 a brief history of major product innovations in 21 categories of processed food products was presented. The sources of each of these product innovations were identified, insofar as possible, from published information. A summary of the sources of product innovations is given in Tables 4-1 and 4-2. For purposes of analyzing changes in the sources of innovation, the chronology has been divided into four periods:

- *The Early Development Period,* prior to 1900, during which the original versions of many processed foods were invented.

- *The Pre-World War II Period*, 1900–1938, which was characterized by a relatively low rate of product innovation.
- *World War II*, 1939–1945, during which a number of new products were developed specifically for military needs.
- *The Post-World War II Period*, which has been characterized by high levels of consumer income and increasing emphasis on innovation as a way of life in American industry.

Comparison of each period with earlier periods clearly shows the shift from individual inventors and small companies to large food processors as the primary source of new products.

TABLE 4-1

Primary Sources of Product Innovations in Selected Processed Food Categories Prior to World War II

Primary Source of Innovation	Early Development Period: Prior to 1900	Pre-World War II Period: 1900–1938
INDIVIDUAL INVENTORS	Cold Breakfast Cereals (1890's) Canned Vegetables (1810) Condensed & Evaporated Milk (1853, 1885) Margarine (1869) Peanut Butter (late 19th Century)	Frozen Vegetables (1920's) Soluble Coffee (c. 1900)
SMALL FOOD PROCESSING COMPANIES	Dry Pet Foods (1855) Packaged Pudding Mixes (1878) Packaged Gelatin Desserts (1897)	Cake Mixes (1931) Canned Pet Foods (1925)
LARGE FOOD PROCESSING COMPANIES	(none known)	(none known)
NONFOOD COMPANIES	(none known)	(none known)
GOVERNMENT AGENCIES	(none known)	(none known)

TABLE 4-2

Primary Sources of Product Innovations in Selected Processed Food Categories: 1939–1964

Primary Source of Innovation	World War II: 1939–1945	Post-World War II Period:	
		1946–1959	1960–1964
INDIVIDUAL INVENTORS	Precooked Rice (1944)[a]	(none known)	(none known)
SMALL FOOD PROCESSING COMPANIES	(none known)	Boil-in-Bag Frozen Vegetables (late 1950's) Corn Oil Margarine (1958) Frozen Dinners (late 1940's) Instant Puddings (1948) Powdered Dairy Creamers (1952)	(none known)
LARGE FOOD PROCESSING COMPANIES	Granular Dehydrated Potatoes[b] Nonfat Dry Milk (1942)	Presweetened Cold Cereals (1949) Nutritional Cereals (1955)	Cereals with Freeze-Dried Fruit (1964) Instant Hot

	Precooked Rice (1944)[c]	Specialty Dehydrated Potatoes (1959–1960) Extruded Dry Pet Foods (1956)	Cereals (1964) Semimoist Pet Foods (1963) Instant-Blending Flour (1963) Synthetic Juice Concentrate (1963) Soft Margarine (1964) Specialty Rice Products (1960's) Powdered Synthetic Creamers (1962) Freeze-Dry Soluble Coffee (1964)
NONFOOD COMPANIES	Frozen Juice Concentrates (1944–1946)[c]	Liquid Dietary Products (1959)	(none known)
GOVERNMENT AGENCIES	Granular Dehydrated Potatoes[b] Frozen Juice Concentrates (1944–1946)[c]	Flaked Dehydrated Potatoes (1956)	(none known)

[a], [b], [c] Product innovations credited jointly to two sources.

Individual Inventors

Prior to 1900 most of the innovations in food processing were contributed by individual inventors. Thus, it was Nicolas Appert, working alone at home for almost 15 years, who developed the canning process of food preservation. Similarly, Post and Kellogg, a patient and an employee in a Battle Creek sanitarium, saw the commercial possibilities of the "health food" which became ready-to-eat breakfast cereal. Perhaps the last of the line of "great inventors" was Clarence Birdseye, who developed a practical process for preservation by freezing in the 1920's.

The reasons for the declining role of the individual inventor are illustrated by the experience of Ataullah Durrani, the originator of precooked rice. Duranni was able to demonstrate the feasibility of his process, but he found that he could not proceed beyond this point to large-scale commercialization without greater technical and financial resources than he could command as an individual.[1] Hence, he joined forces with the General Foods Corporation in 1944.

Small Food Processors

Prior to 1900 there were very few really *large* food processing companies, at least by present standards. The smaller firms of that day (some of them predecessors of present-day large concerns) contributed many of the product innovations which were introduced in the 19th century and in the pre-World War II era (see Table 4-1). Dry pet food, packaged gelatin desserts, and packaged pudding mixes were all introduced by small firms prior to 1900, while canned pet foods and cake mixes were pioneered by small companies during the 1900–1938 period.

Even after World War II small processors continued to play an important role with such new products as frozen dinners, instant pudding mixes, and powdered (dairy-based) coffee creamers. Throughout the 1950's, however, the increasing advantages

---

[1] It is a moot point, of course, whether Durrani "could" have carried precooked rice to a successful conclusion without the aid of General Foods. It is virtually certain, however, that the further development and introduction of the product would have taken much longer.

of large firms in R&D and in marketing came to overshadow the efforts of small firms. It is interesting to note that large firms now dominate the markets for at least four of the five products initially developed by small firms between 1946 and 1959 (see Table 4-2). In two cases (boil-in-bag frozen vegetables and corn oil margarine) the success of the larger firms may be attributed at least in part to superior *marketing* skills and resources. In the other two cases, however, large processors entered the market with significant *technical* improvements on the products originally introduced by small firms. Thus, the first powdered coffee creamer, Pream, was introduced by M & R Dietetics Laboratories in 1952. This dairy-based formulation was later superseded by a nondairy coffee creamer introduced by the Carnation Company. Instant puddings, introduced by American Maize Products in 1948, originally were based on amioca starch. Subsequent versions of the product, introduced by Standard Brands and General Foods in the early 1950's, had a potato starch base which yielded a firmer, more satisfactory result to the consumer.

Large Food Processors

While small food processors contributed a substantial share of the product innovations prior to 1959, the dominance of the large firms is clear cut after 1960. Large processors introduced all nine of the product innovations between 1960 and 1964, as shown in Table 4-2. Although some of these products, such as specialty packaged rice products, may be regarded as much less fundamental innovations than earlier developments, others are clearly significant departures in technology from existing products. Semimoist pet foods, for example, are based on a whole new technique of food preservation in which enough of the moisture content of a food—in this case, meat—is removed to retard spoilage. Similarly, synthetic orange juice concentrate is one of the first really successful simulations of a natural product, and instant-blending flour is significantly different in texture and performance from conventional all-purpose flours.

The dominance of large food processors in product innovation during the post-World War II period, as shown in Table 4-2, has not generally been recognized. It is widely believed that small firms and government agencies are responsible for most real innovations, and that large firms pre-empt the markets for the resulting products simply by means of superior financial resources and/or marketing skills. Thus, for example, the Federal Trade Commission has asserted that

> . . . few of these "new [food] products" are the result of even moderately complex technologies, and essentially all of the more complex technologies were developed with public funds. The initial producers of most of these new products were characteristically smaller firms. Large firms typically entered these areas through acquisition.[2]

While this statement may be a reasonably accurate description of the process of innovation prior to the 1950's, it does not appear to be a realistic characterization of the period since the late 1950's. As shown in a later part of this chapter, R&D expenditures by large processors increased sharply during the late 1950's. This fact, together with the record of new products introduced between 1960 and 1964, suggests that the large firms are increasingly responsible for product innovation in a technical sense as well as in terms of such marketing actions as advertising, packaging, and distribution.

Nonfood Companies

Innovation in food processing by companies in other industries has never been a major source of new products, as shown in Tables 4-1 and 4-2. One major innovation, frozen orange juice concentrate, was developed jointly by a nonfood company (National Research Corporation) and a governmental agency (Florida Citrus Commission). Since World War II the only new product introduced by a nonfood company in the categories studied was Metrecal, the original "dietary weight control" product. As in other past cases of innovation by drug firms, Metrecal was originally conceived as a health aid rather than a food, and its success as a food product was in a sense accidental.

---

[2] National Commission on Food Marketing, *The Structure of Food Manufacturing*, Technical Study No. 8 (Washington, Government Printing Office, 1966), p. 81.

Government Agencies

Government agencies, especially those within the U.S. Department of Agriculture, have long played an important part in the process of food processing innovation. The conclusion stated above regarding the role of large food processors is not intended to imply that governmental agencies make *no* contribution to the development of new foods. It is, however, difficult to identify more than a few specific products currently being consumed in large volume that have resulted directly from USDA research. During the post-World War II period USDA studies have provided the basis for instant sweet potato flakes, instant pumpkin products, freeze-dried fruits, and low-fat ripened cheeses. As shown in Table 4-2, USDA research earlier yielded the flaked version of dehydrated potatoes, which has since become the most widely used processing method.

Much of the research carried on by governmental agencies is directed toward more basic types of studies than those carried on by most food processors. In the mid-1960's the U.S. Department of Agriculture operated 19 separate laboratories devoted solely to basic research. Similarly, the Quartermaster Corps of the Department of the Army has played a leading role in experimental work on preservation by irradiation. Thus far, however, this research has not had a major impact on the product assortment available to American consumers.

Research and Development Activities

The remainder of this chapter deals with R&D activities of large food processing firms. Research, development, and associated product-testing activities are time-consuming, costly, and risky activities for processing firms. These activities precede, and make possible, the introduction of new products, as described in Chapter 5.

Research and Development Expenditures

The rapid growth of R&D expenditures has been one of the most significant trends in the American economy during the 1950's and 1960's. According to the National Science Foundation, total R&D spending more than tripled between 1953 and 1962, from $3.6 billion to $11.5 billion.³ By 1966 total planned expenditures were estimated by the Economics Department of McGraw-Hill Publishing Company at $15.2 billion, and a further increase to $18.2 billion was predicted for 1969.⁴

Research and development expenditures by food processing companies are small relative to the amounts spent by manufacturers of aircraft, machinery, and chemicals, but they have increased sharply during the 1950's and 1960's. In 1954 total R&D expenditures by firms in the "Food and Kindred Products" industries were estimated by NSF at $64 million. The corresponding figure for 1966, as estimated by McGraw-Hill, was $157 million. Thus, the percentage increase in food processors' R&D spending between 1956 and 1966 (145%) was almost twice as great as that of industry in general (75%). Notwithstanding the rapid growth of R&D in the food industries, the ratio of such expenditures to net sales was much lower in 1962 (0.3%) than for industry in general (4.1%).⁵

A very large proportion of R&D expenditures is made by a relatively small number of large firms, both in the food processing industries and in industry generally. In 1962, 86% of all R&D funds were spent by companies with 5,000 or more employees; the corresponding figure for the food industry was 76%.⁶ Almost all the companies that provided information for this study were drawn from this group of very large food processing firms. Expenditures

---

³ National Science Foundation, *Basic Research, Applied Research and Development in Industry*, 1962, NSF 65–18 (Washington, Government Printing Office, 1965), p. 94. The NSF estimates are based on annual mail surveys of samples of manufacturing firms. The figures cited include expenditures on "basic" research, i.e., investigations which do not have specific commercial objectives, as well as the costs of "applied research" and "development," which are aimed at the development and/or improvement of *products* or *processes*.

⁴ *Business Week*, May 7, 1966, p. 164. The McGraw-Hill estimates for 1966 were based on a survey of manufacturers, designed to be comparable with the NSF surveys.

⁵ National Science Foundation, *op. cit.*, p. 122. More than half of the R&D expenditures for industry in general were government-financed, compared with only 4% for the food industries. Even with allowance for this factor, the rate of R&D spending by food companies was one-sixth as great (in relation to sales) as the average for all industries.

⁶ *Ibid.*, p. 96.

for R&D by the 17 companies that provided such information are summarized in Table 4-3. As shown there, R&D spending by large processors increased much more rapidly than did sales volume over the period 1954–1964. Total R&D expenditures more than doubled, while aggregate sales rose by 32%. The increase in R&D outlays was especially marked between 1958 and 1960. Since 1960 the percentage of sales allocated to research and development has increased only slightly.

TABLE 4-3

Aggregate Sales and Aggregate Research & Development Expenditures, 17 Large Food Processing Firms: 1954–1964

Year	Aggregate Sales (000)	R&D Expenditures (000)	% of Sales
1954	$4,974,237	$18,275	0.37%
1956	5,215,453	20,341	0.39
1958	5,600,947	24,026	0.43
1960	5,636,042	30,322	0.54
1962	6,005,665	34,222	0.57
1964	6,579,563	39,611	0.60

Source: Based on responses to Question 1, Schedule A, of the survey questionnaire (see Appendix).

The companies represented in Table 4-3 are not, of course, typical of the food processing industries as a whole. For the 17 cooperating firms the ratio of R&D expenditure to sales in 1964 was 0.6%, just double the overall ratio for the food industry estimated by NSF for 1962. The fact that these 17 firms accounted for about one-third of total R&D spending by *all* firms in the food industries is further evidence of the high degree of concentration of R&D activity in large processing organizations.

Earlier in this chapter it was pointed out that large processors have been the predominant source of new food products introduced since 1960. Presumably, the sharp rise in R&D expenditures between 1958 and 1962, reflected in Table 4-3, was one of the major factors lying behind the increased role of the large firms in the development and introduction of new products.

The Product Development and Testing Process

A substantial portion of the expenditures shown in Table 4-3 is devoted to ongoing research activity, much of which is properly designated as basic research.[7] Especially in the very large companies, continuing efforts are devoted to research on various aspects of food chemistry, food preservation, flavor, and other subjects which are not directly related to specific new *product* objectives. Ultimately, however, this type of research is justified by its long-term contribution to the development of profitable new products.

The results of basic research activities can seldom be translated directly and immediately into salable new products. Standing between the two is the sequence of technical and managerial activities involved in *developing* and *testing* new products. This sequence of activities commences with a search for product *ideas*, passes through various stages of research, development, testing, modification, further testing, etc., and *sometimes* culminates in the successful marketing of a product through normal channels of trade. The purpose of this section is to summarize the information about large food processors' practices in the development and testing of distinctly new products, which was reported in the responses to the survey questionnaire (see Appendix).[8] The activities and costs described in the remainder of this chapter include only those that occur *prior* to the introduction of a new product.

Sources of Product Ideas

Although new food products may grow out of ongoing basic research programs, the history of an individual product really begins with the formulation of a product *idea* or *concept*. Ideas for new products are sometimes obtained fortuitously, e.g., by unsolicited suggestions or by accidental discoveries. More often, however, they result from systematic, organized search efforts on the part of processing companies.

---

[7] According to the McGraw-Hill estimates, $20 million out of the $157 million expenditure planned for 1966 by food processors, or about 13% of the total, was devoted to basic research.

[8] As defined in Chapter 2, distinctly new products are those which are substantially different in form, ingredients, or processing methods from other products previously marketed by a *given* company.

TABLE 4-4

**Sources of Ideas for 127 Distinctly New Food Products
Introduced Between 1954 and 1964**

Type of Source	% of All Products	
INTERNAL COMPANY SOURCES:	89%*	
R&D activities		67%
Sales personnel		16
Other		15
DIRECT CONTACT WITH CONSUMERS:	34	
New product survey research		21
Open-end discussions with consumers		10
Other marketing research		19
Unsolicited suggestions		6
INDIRECT CONTACT WITH CONSUMERS:	5	
Distributors' personnel, trade or consumer magazines, etc.		5
OTHER EXTERNAL SOURCES:	35	
Competitors		23
Advertising agencies		8
Suppliers, consultants, government agencies		5
Because of multiple sources, the total of the figures shown is		195%

* Unduplicated total for category. For example, *one or more* internal sources were mentioned for 89% of the 127 distinct new products covered by the survey.

SOURCE: Responses to Question 4, Schedule B of survey (see Appendix).

The sources of ideas for the 127 *distinctly new* processed food products covered in the survey are shown in Table 4-4. In most cases, more than one source was identified for a given product; the average, in fact, is just under two per product.

Sources of new product ideas have been grouped, in Table 4-4, into four main categories: those *within* the company (such as R&D activities); those involving direct contact with consumers; indirect contacts with consumers; and other external sources. Among these four categories, sources within processing companies were most frequently mentioned; ideas for two-thirds of all the products came at least in part from research and development activities. Other internal sources, including sales personnel, contributed to 31% of all product ideas. Even allowing for duplication among the three categories of internal sources, the ideas for nearly 9 out of 10 of the 127 distinctly new products came in part from *within* the processing companies. At the same time over one-third involved ideas obtained from direct contact with consumers, primarily through formalized marketing research investigations, and 40% were based in part on ideas from other external sources. Thus, it seems reasonable to say that the typical new product represents a marriage of ideas resulting from R&D *and* external sources of information and inspiration.

It is apparently rare for the consumer to take the initiative in expressing her desires; only 6% of the products involved such unsolicited suggestions. It is somewhat more surprising to find that new products were so seldom (5%) based on ideas from such outside organizations as government agencies.

Stages of Product Development

Once an idea for a new product has been accepted, it usually must pass through a process of development before it can be "translated" into a finished product. *In general* this process may be viewed as consisting of a series of stages, in which completion of each stage usually (but not universally) serves as a precedent to the beginning of the next stage of the sequence.

The activities involved in product research, development, testing, and introduction can be classified into five major stages, as follows:

Stage of Product Development	General Description of Activities Encompassed
Research & Development	Research, design, engineering, and technical specifications, manufacture of prototypes and similar activities involving technical development.
Product Testing	Testing of consumer reactions or evaluation of the product prior to offering the product for sale in the market place.
Test Marketing	Offering the product for sale in one or more regional or local market areas on a test basis only.

Limited Area
Introduction

Offering the product for sale in one or more regions or areas, comprising something less than a company's total marketing area.

Full-Scale
Introduction

Introduction in substantially all areas in which a company normally distributes its products.

During each of these stages a new product is subjected to periodic review and evaluation by management. At any point a decision may be made to discontinue work on a product or to devote more or less effort to its further development. During the R&D phase product *concepts* and samples of products are evaluated primarily by "judgmental" methods, but also to some extent by marketing research techniques. The product-testing and test-marketing stages are, of course, designed primarily for purposes of determining whether a new product should be introduced and, if so, how it should be marketed.

Only a fraction of the products which begin a given stage in the development-and-testing process survive and pass through to the next stage.

An indication of the mortality rates for product ideas at the R&D and product-testing stages is given by the results of a survey of 38 food processors conducted by Christopher Smith of Arthur D. Little, Inc.[9] Smith asked executives of the processing companies to estimate the percentages of all new product ideas that are rejected on the basis of (1) formal consumer testing, i.e., product concept tests, or (2) informal evaluations. The responses indicated that, of *all* product ideas which received any explicit evaluation,

- 19% were accepted for further development and/or testing;
- 41% were rejected on the basis of formal tests;
- 40% were rejected on the basis of informal evaluations.

Of the new product ideas which were accepted at the first stage, Smith's survey indicates that 71% were rejected at the product-testing stage, either on the basis of informal consumer tests or via

[9] Christopher Smith, "A Sample Survey of Food Processors' Assessments of Consumer Needs When Introducing New Products," research report submitted to the National Commission on Food Marketing on behalf of Grocery Manufacturers of America, Inc. (Cambridge, Massachusetts, 1966).

Figure 4-1. Stages of Product Development: All Categories
(124 Products)

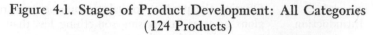

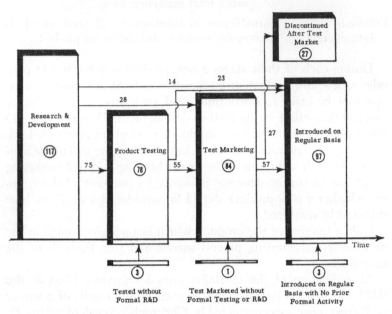

formal testing. Thus, out of every 1,000 new product ideas coming out of R&D and other sources, it appears that only 55 (29% of 19% = 5.5%) survive both preliminary evaluations *and* product testing. (These estimates include product-line extensions and product improvements as well as distinctly new products.)

Information about distinctly new products that were introduced to the market between 1954 and 1964, on a test-marketing basis and/or for regular distribution, was obtained in the survey of processing companies described in Chapter 1. A synopsis of the history of 124 such products is shown in Figure 4-1. Similar flow charts are shown in Figures 4-2 through 4-6 for the five product categories in which sufficient data were obtained to permit separate reporting.[10]

---

[10] To avoid disclosure of data for individual companies to other companies participating in the survey, no figures are reported for product categories in which fewer than three firms supplied information.

Figure 4-2. Stages of Product Development: Cold Breakfast
Cereals
(20 Products)

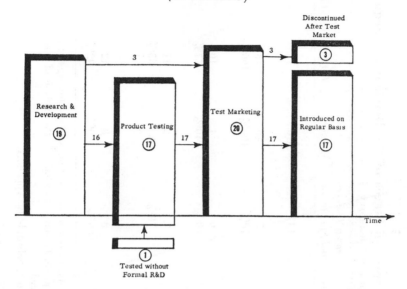

Examination of the data in these charts quickly reveals that not *all* products pass through *all* stages of development. In many instances, products apparently bypass or skip one or more developmental stages. One can speculate on the reasons for bypassing steps in the development process. The *costs* (both in money and in time) of conducting any of the developmental stages can be substantial. Presumably, when a product bypasses a stage, those responsible for its development have judged that the *value* to be gained from conducting activities in that stage is not sufficient to justify the costs involved.

A summary of the developmental stages undergone by the 124 distinctly new products is presented in Table 4-5. For all categories combined, it can be seen that the stage most frequently bypassed is that of product testing. Only 63% of products in all categories underwent product testing, most of the remainder going directly from research and development into test marketing or regular distribution. A slightly higher percentage of products

TABLE 4-5

Number of Products Passing Through Specified Stages of the Development Sequence, by Product Category

Product Development Stage	Breakfast Cereals—Cold	Cake Mixes	Frozen Dinners and Specialties	Margarine	Pet Foods	All Categories
Total Number of Products Introduced	20	14	10	10	13	124*
R&D						
No. Passing Through	19	14	7	10	13	117
% of Total	95%	100%	70%	100%	100%	94%
Product Testing						
No. Passing Through	17	10	6	4	10	78
% of Total	85%	71%	60%	40%	77%	63%
Test Marketing						
No. Passing Through	20	13	7	8	11	84
% of Total	100%	93%	70%	80%	85%	68%
Discontinued after Test	3	5	1	2	1	27
Regular Distribution						
Number Introduced	17	9	8	8	12	97
% of Total	85%	64%	80%	80%	92%	78%

* Of the 127 distinctly new products studied, 3 were extremely recent introductions still undergoing test marketing. These 3 products (including one cold cereal and one dog food product) were *not* included in the analysis of stages of product development, leaving a total of 124 products to be examined.

Source: Responses to survey questionnaire, Question 5, Schedule B, Appendix.

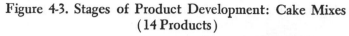

Figure 4-3. Stages of Product Development: Cake Mixes
(14 Products)

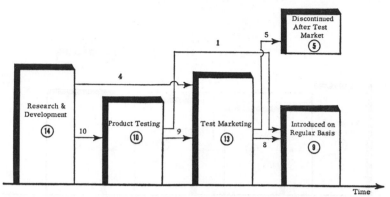

(68%) underwent test marketing. Nearly all products underwent *some* form of consumer evaluation prior to regular introduction by means of product testing, test marketing, or both. Only 17 of the 124 products (14% of the total) bypassed *both* product testing and test marketing.

Comparison of the developmental histories of individual product categories reveals substantial differences among them. Cold breakfast cereals (Figure 4-2) and pet foods (Figure 4-4) most often passed through the complete developmental sequence. Apparently, cold cereals and pet food products require very considerable developmental effort, suggesting both technological complexity (in processing and/or ingredients) and higher-than-average uncertainty as to consumer acceptance of new products in these categories. Extremely strong emphasis was placed on consumer evaluation; only one of the 33 products examined in the two categories failed to undergo product testing or test marketing, while 26 new products were subjected to both product testing *and* test marketing. It is also noteworthy that the proportion of products eventually achieving regular distribution was higher in both cold cereals and pet food than in any other category studied.

Quite different from the above pattern is that observed in a category such as frozen dinners and specialties, as shown in Figure 4-5. Here, there is no clear pattern of new product development; very

Figure 4-4. Stages of Product Development: Pet Foods
(13 Products)

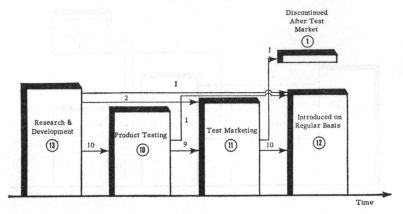

few products pass through all stages of development. The high interchange of technology between old and new products is demonstrated by the fact that 3 of the 10 studied underwent *no* formal research and development activities. Only 5 of the 10 received both product testing *and* test marketing. One new frozen dinner and specialty product was placed directly into full distribution, with no prior formal development of any kind. Notwithstanding, the manufacturer of this product has described it as being "moderately successful."

In contrast to cold cereals and pet foods, the pattern of development of frozen dinner and specialty products might well be described as informal, in that one, two, or more developmental stages are often bypassed entirely. Similar patterns were typical in biscuits, cookies, and crackers; canned vegetables; and frozen vegetables, although the number of reported cases was not sufficient to permit separate reporting of each of these categories. Clearly, however, new products in all these categories are generally characterized by great similarity to existing products, in terms of both the technology of processing and (presumably) the predictability of ultimate consumer evaluation in the marketplace.

The figures given in Table 4-5, together with the results of Smith's survey cited earlier in this chapter, provide a basis for es-

Figure 4-5. Stages of Product Development: Frozen Dinners and Specialties
(10 Products)

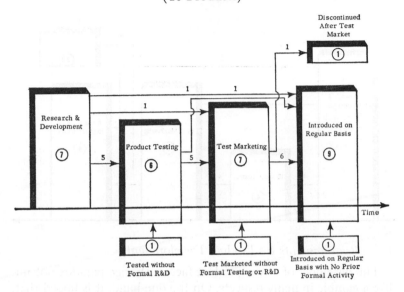

timating the results of the evaluations that are made of new food products at each stage in the development and testing process. Among large food processors, it appears that of every 1,000 new product ideas:

810 are rejected at the idea stage, about half by informal means and about half on the basis of formal consumer tests;

135 are rejected on the basis of product tests, either formal or informal;

12 are discontinued after test marketing;

43 are introduced to the market on a regular basis.[11]

---

[11] The first two figures come directly from Smith's estimates, as explained above. The estimate of products discontinued after test marketing in relation to total product ideas is based on the data in Table 4-5. It is assumed that the 124 products introduced on a test-market *and/or* regular basis (Table 4-5) correspond to the 55 products out of 1,000 which Smith reported as surviving earlier evaluations.

Figure 4-6. Stages of Product Development: Margarine
(10 Products)

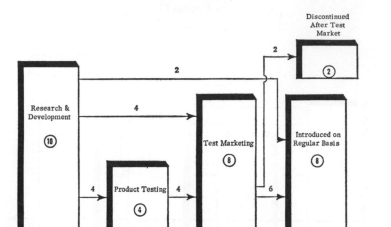

Time Requirements for Product Development

The developer of a new product faces a strange paradox not unlike a gamble in many respects. On the one hand, it is hoped that, by being among the first to offer a product with innovative features, he will capture the consumer's allegiance and reap the appropriate rewards. Thus, having once acquired a seemingly good idea for a new product, it behooves a manufacturer to translate that idea into a tangible reality before his competitors do so ahead of him. At the same time, however, every manufacturer is well aware that a prematurely launched product can result in disaster. If greater effort is devoted to developing and testing an innovation prior to its regular introduction, it is presumed that the chances of consumer acceptance will increase.

The amount of time spent in developing a new product, then, substantially influences its ultimate profitability. Too long a period of development may result in foregone sales and profit opportunities. Too short a period, with its concomitant premature introduction, may result in substantial losses. For the 127 distinctly new products examined in our survey, the average time spent in each of the stages of product development is shown in Table 4-6.

TABLE 4-6

Average Number of Months Spent in Each Stage of Development Before Proceeding to Next Stage*

Product Category	R&D	Product Testing	Test Market	Limited Distribution	Total Months from First Activity to Achieve Limited Distribution	Total Months from First Activity to Achieve Full Distribution
Breakfast Cereals—Cold	32	14	6	5	56†	55
Cake Mixes	15	9	6	11	22	29
Frozen Dinners and Specialties	18	13	12	12	22	41
Margarine	15	9	10	8	23	33
Pet Foods	11	9	14	9	29	40
All Product Categories (including those above)	18	11	10	10	32	37
Seven Pioneering Products	16	13	16	10	33	43

* Averages are based only on those products which actually underwent a stage, and do *not* include products which skipped the stage in question.

† The average number of months required for cold breakfast cereals to attain limited distribution is greater than that required to attain full distribution because some products were placed immediately into full distribution, and these products apparently required less than average time to complete earlier steps in the development and testing sequence.

SOURCE: Responses to survey questionnaire, Question 5, Schedule B, Appendix.

For all categories combined, an average of just over three years (37 months) is required to move from the start of formal developmental activities to full distribution. (This average is based on reported histories for those products which achieved full distribution, and does not allow for casualties along the way.)

Among the various stages leading to regular introduction of a new product, the first is the most time-consuming. An average of 18 months was required in research and development before activities in the next stage could begin. Ironically, it is that stage most remote from the ultimate test of fire, the offering of the new product for sale in the marketplace, that requires the greatest investment in time.

Among the various product categories, the time spent in developing cold cereal products stands out clearly as considerably greater than average. From first developmental activity to the point of achieving full distribution, a new cold cereal product took an average of 55 months, 50% higher than the comparable figure for all categories combined. It will be recalled that cold cereal products tended to pass through *all* stages of development, and no doubt this full sequence contributes to a longer period of development. A very substantial amount of the developmental period, however, may be attributed to the time required in the research and development of cold cereal products. For this stage an average of 32 months was required before proceeding to the next stage, as compared with an average of 18 months for all categories combined. (Both averages include only those products which actually underwent the stage, and *not* those which bypassed it.)

Separate figures are given in Table 4-6 for a group of seven pioneering products. Each of the products in this group was the first or second brand to be introduced of a new *type* of food product. As explained in Chapter 2, a new type of product is one which involves form, ingredients, or methods of preservation not previously available to the market. For example, one of the pioneering products represented in Table 4-6 is one of the first two nutritional breakfast cereals; another is one of the first two corn oil margarines.

The total time required to achieve full distribution for pioneering products was slightly higher (43 months) than the average for all distinctly new products. Somewhat surprisingly, however, the average time required for the R&D stage was actually *lower* for pioneering products than the average for all products combined. The figure shown in Table 4-6 for R&D may be somewhat misleading, in that almost all the pioneering products were based on previous work carried on as basic research or in connection with other products. The average of 16 months includes only the time spent on project activities specifically associated with the products in question.

The biggest difference in time requirements for pioneering products is in the *test marketing* stage of the development and testing process. Apparently the greater "newness" of these products implies a need for more time to evaluate market acceptance.

Costs of Product Development

Among the most important categories of expenditures prior to introduction are those incurred for R&D and for marketing research. Just as the search for ideas involved an interplay of technology and consumer demand, so too does the process of development.

Average expenditures *per product* for R&D and for marketing research, for 111 of the 127 distinctly new products covered by the survey, are shown in Table 4-7. The R&D figures given in the table include only those expenditures *directly* attributable to a *specific* new product. In most cases, new products also benefit from more basic research activities for which no costs are explicitly allocated to the products. For example, one of the respondent firms introduced a corn oil margarine during the period covered by the study. The R&D work on this particular product was in large measure an outgrowth of continuing research by the company on the properties of various fats and oils. Similarly, one company's development of a semimoist dog food was a partial outgrowth of its basic research on the low-moisture preservation of foods generally.

For all product categories combined, average pre-introduction expenditures per product on R&D and marketing research amounted to $68,000 and $26,000, respectively. These figures make no allowance for capital *investments* prior to introduction, which are often substantial.

Differences in average pre-introduction expenditures among the product categories shown in Table 4-7 reflect basic differences in processing technologies. In some product fields, such as cake mixes and frozen dinners and specialties, new products can be developed *without* major changes in production techniques, equipment, or types of ingredients. The same is true, generally speaking, of biscuits, cookies, and crackers; canned vegetables; and frozen vegetables. (Separate figures are not given for these categories in Table 4-7 because the numbers of cases were too small.) In contrast, average R&D expenditures for new products in the cold cereal, margarine, and pet food categories were typically much higher than for those just mentioned. Average expenditures per product for marketing research tended to be highest in the *same* categories for which R&D costs were high. It is not clear to what extent both types of expenditures are related to common underlying differences, e.g., variations in technical complexity, and to what extent companies tend to spend more on marketing research *because* a greater R&D commitment has been undertaken.

For the seven pioneering products for which the data were available, average pre-introduction expenditures were substantially higher than the average for all products. Research and development expenditures ($127,000 per product) were nearly twice as great as average, while marketing research outlays were nearly three times as great.

The expenditures shown in Table 4-7 do *not* include R&D or marketing research costs incurred during a test-marketing program. The cost of conducting a test market, however, should be regarded as a very real cost of development, for it is only after the test-marketing results are known that the final decision to introduce the product is made. Indeed, as later discussion in this report will reveal, that decision in many instances is negative. The manufacturer must then bear the burden of test-marketing losses, as well as other developmental expenditures, with no hope of recouping them from the product in question.

The "cost" of test marketing is an elusive concept, defying precise definition. For our purposes, the best available measure would appear to be the net dollar loss incurred in conducting test-mar-

TABLE 4-7

Average Expenditures per Product for Research and Development and for Marketing Research, by Product Category

Product Category	Product R&D*	Marketing Research*	No. of Products†	No. of Companies
Breakfast Cereals—Cold	$122,000	$60,000	21	6
Cake Mixes	27,000	13,000	3	3
Frozen Dinners and Specialties	15,000	8,000	9	5
Margarine	65,000	17,000	10	4
Pet Foods	91,000	37,000	13	7
All Product Categories (including those above)	$ 68,000	$26,000	111	19
Seven Pioneering Products	127,000	76,000	7	6

* Includes only expenses specifically charged to the individual products covered.

† Of the 127 distinctly new products analyzed in this report, there were 16 for which manufacturers were unable to provide data on pre-introduction expenditures for product research and development or marketing research. Thus, this table reports results for a total of 111 distinctly new products only.

SOURCE: Responses to Question 10a, Schedule B, Appendix.

keting operations. More precisely, we define the *net negative contribution* during test marketing as follows:

Net Negative = Gross Profit from Test-Market Sales, minus costs for
Contribution   Marketing, Research & Development, and Marketing Research incurred during test marketing.

No allowance is made in the computation of contribution for *fixed costs*, even those wholly associated with the individual product (e.g., fixed costs of operating processing equipment). As a result, the net negative contribution figure is an understatement of the full cost of test marketing.

Average costs of test marketing, as represented by net negative contributions during test-marketing operations, are shown in Table 4-8. Not all manufacturers maintained records of test-marketing operations, and the figures shown are thus computed only on the basis of available data for 72 products.

The figures in Table 4-8 reveal that test marketing can be an extremely expensive developmental stage. For all categories combined the average net negative contribution from test-marketing

Table 4-8

Average Net Negative Contribution per Product During Test-Marketing Operations, by Product Category

Product Category	Average Negative Contribution per Product	Number of Products	Number of Companies
Breakfast Cereals—Cold	$921,000	11	6
Cake Mixes	61,000	10	3
Frozen Dinners and Specialties	47,000	4	3
Pet Foods	531,000	10	6
All Product Categories (including those above)	$248,000	72	13
Pioneering Products	592,000	4	4

Source: Sales and expenditure data reported in Question 10, Schedule B, Appendix.

operations was $248,000 per product. Cold cereals ($921,000) and pet food ($531,000) once again substantially exceeded the average, while cake mixes ($61,000) and frozen dinners and specialties ($47,000) were well below the average.

Estimates of net negative contribution during test marketing are available for just four of the pioneering products. As shown in Table 4-8, the average negative contribution per product was $592,000, considerably more than twice as great as the average for *all* products. Presumably the high cost of test marketing for pioneering products is due, at least in part, to the longer duration of test-market operations for such products as shown in Table 4-6.

Summary

In summary, the typical position of a food processor who has developed and tested a new product *up to the point* of regular introduction to the market may be described as follows:

- Ideas for the new product were obtained both from R&D personnel within the company and from marketing research;
- The product has probably passed through stages of formal R&D, product testing, *and* market testing, although one or more of these stages may have been bypassed;
- About three years have passed since formal R&D activity on the product was initiated;
- On the average, costs of $68,000 for R&D and $26,000 for marketing research have been incurred, and some capital investment has also been made. If the product was test marketed, an additional average cost of $248,000 has been incurred during test-market operations.

It is from such a position that the large processing firm proceeds to the next step, that of getting distribution and introducing the new product via advertising, promotion, and selling. These introductory marketing activities, and the resulting patterns of sales and dollar contributions, are described in the next chapter.

CHAPTER 5

New Product Introduction

In the preceding chapter we have described some of the activities involved in the development and testing of new processed food products. All these activities take place *prior to* the introduction of a product to the marketplace. Once it has been decided to introduce a product on a regular basis, the processor must plan and execute an introductory marketing campaign. Usually introductory marketing efforts are very costly and there is great uncertainty about the strategy and tactics that should be employed, even when test-marketing research has been conducted. This uncertainty is not typically resolved until long after the date of introduction, because the patterns of sales, costs, and profits for a new product are extremely difficult to predict.

This chapter deals with the practices of large food processing companies in introducing distinctly new products to the market and with typical patterns of sales and expenditures during the first few years of regular distribution. A major purpose of the chapter is to provide information relevant to the evaluation of the success and failure of distinctly new food products and to show the relationships between new product performance and various factors which may affect it.

Introductory Marketing

Even before a new product has been fully tested and evaluated, plans are usually being made for an introductory marketing campaign. Most large food processors have long ago accepted the fact that no matter how novel a better mousetrap may be, extensive and skillful promotion is necessary to inform and persuade consumers and distributors.

Functions of Introductory Promotion

It is generally recognized that the functions of advertising, personal selling, and other forms of promotion are significantly different and more complicated for a new product than for established products. To illustrate some of the differences, excerpts from the marketing plans for Brand X, a processed food product, during its *first* and *sixth* years of regular distribution, are shown in Table 5-1. The product in question was the second brand of a new type of food product, and was introduced about two years after the pioneering brand. On the basis of several consumer surveys, the company which introduced Brand X concluded that the size

TABLE 5-1

Excerpts from Marketing Plans for Brand X: Year of Introduction vs. Sixth Year of Regular Distribution

Introductory Year	*Sixth Year*
1. . . . our primary objective should be to induce the maximum possible growth of the total market.	1. Marketing objectives:
2. First month (Get distribution): Introduce with 100,000 units of "one free with one" factory banded deal pack . . . we would also have a 25¢ per case deal on the regular pack for the first 30 days to stimulate retail stocking.	a. To increase share of market to ——% [and thus] sell at least —— units. . . .
	b. To improve consumer acceptance through product improvement.
3. Second month (Introduce to consumers): The second month will be devoted to a *major* introductory advertising effort.	2. Promotional objectives:
	a. To increase frequency of use among the hard core of current customers. . . .
4. Throughout the balance of the first 12 months, we would maintain strong promotion. . . . We would also schedule at least 4 more special sales force coverages . . . to insure added distribution and adequate retail stocks.	b. To attract new as well as former customers through special recipe promotions. . . .
	c. To increase share of market by drawing away users from competitive brands. . . .

of the total market for the product could be increased substantially. As a result the primary objective for the introductory marketing program was to expand primary demand. As shown in Table 5-1, the specific objectives set for the first year were to get retail distribution, to induce consumer trial via reduced prices, and to expand on these beachheads by continued high levels of advertising and sales effort.

By its sixth year of regular distribution the product had an established place in its market—it was, in fact, the leading brand—and the total market was no longer expanding rapidly. Accordingly, the objectives shown in Table 5-1 for Year 6 are quite different from those of the introductory year. The emphasis has shifted to *competitive* promotion and, to a lesser extent, to seeking relatively minor changes in consumer behavior such as new uses of the product in special recipes.

The promotional methods used in the introductory marketing of Brand X reflect the tasks which must be performed in introducing any new food product:

1. Informing consumers of the existence of the new product and of its distinctive features;
2. Persuading consumers to try the new product, usually through temporary price reductions, samples, coupons, or other direct inducements to purchase;
3. Inducing retailers and distributors to stock the product, usually through temporary discounts and promotional allowances;
4. Maintaining distribution after initial orders have been secured.

Costs of Introductory Marketing

Because so many difficult functions must be performed to introduce a new product effectively, the costs of introductory marketing are much greater than the costs of marketing established food products. Average expenditures per product for marketing the 127 distinctly new food products covered by the survey are summarized in Table 5-2. This table shows average dollar expenditures per product and average ratios of marketing expenditures to sales (at factory prices) for the first and second years of regular distribution. Marketing expenditures, as defined in the Questionnaire Guide, include the costs of *advertising* (media time and space,

TABLE 5-2

Average Marketing Expenditures per Product and Ratios of Marketing Expenditures to Sales for Distinctly New Food Products, by Product Category (Based on Data for 127 Products Introduced (1954–1964)

	First Year of Distribution		Second Year of Distribution	
Product Category	Average Expenditure per Product	Average Ratio of Marketing Expenditures to Sales	Average Expenditure per Product	Average Ratio of Marketing Expenditures to Sales
Breakfast Cereals—Cold	$3,401,000	51%	$1,374,000	30%
Cake Mixes	575,000	61	300,000	57
Frozen Dinners and Specialties	83,000	20	N.A.	N.A.
Margarine	2,003,000	30	2,393,000	22
Pet Foods	1,926,000	49	N.A.	N.A.
All Product Categories (including those above)	$1,407,000	43%	$ 961,000	24%
Seven Pioneering Products	4,911,000	41	3,712,000	22

N.A. = Data not available.

SOURCE: Responses to Question 10, Schedule B, Appendix.

production, and agency compensation); *sales force compensation and/or brokerage fees;* and *sales promotion,* such as product samples, coupons, display materials, and so forth.

The data in Table 5-2 indicate that dollar expenditures per product are about a third lower in the second year after introduction than in the first year, while the ratio of marketing expenditures to sales declines by almost one-half. In both of the first two years, marketing expenditures are much higher *in relation to sales* than those typically incurred for established products. The over-all ratio of marketing costs to sales, for the 17 large processing firms which supplied the relevant data, was approximately 13.5% in 1964. (See Chapter 6.) Thus, the average marketing-to-sales ratio for distinctly new products during the first year of distribution was more than 3.2 times as great as the corresponding ratio for *all* products. The second year marketing-to-sales ratio (24% of sales) was nearly twice as great as that for all products, old and new.

Among the product categories for which separate figures are given in Table 5-2, breakfast cereals, margarine, and pet foods had the highest average dollar expenditures per product. Breakfast cereals and cake mixes had higher-than-average ratios of marketing expenditures to sales. The figures shown for seven pioneering new products show that dollar expenditures per product were much higher than the over-all average. The ratio of expenditures to sales was slightly *below* average, however, because average sales during the first year were more than three times as great for the pioneering new products than for all new food products combined.

The pattern of declining rates of marketing expenditure during the first two years of regular distribution, shown in Table 5-2, reflects two underlying factors. During the first year a new product's sales volume is usually low; hence, marketing expenditures represent a high *proportion* of gross revenue. As the product comes to be accepted—*if* it is accepted—sales volume increases. At the same time average dollar expenditures on marketing are cut back as the distinctive objectives of introductory promotion are achieved. Thus, the decline in the average marketing-to-sales ratio from 43% in Year 1 to 24% in Year 2 reflects both increased sales volume *and* reduced levels of marketing effort.

The changing relationship between marketing expenditures and sales for individual products is generally consistent with the product life cycle pattern which characterizes product *categories*. In a study of product life cycles for various categories of food products, it was found that average annual ratios of advertising expenditure to sales tend to decline as a product category passes through stages of introduction and rapid growth into a stage of maturity.[1] For example, advertising expenditures by producers of dehydrated potatoes represented 21% of total retail sales in 1960, when the product category was growing rapidly; by 1964 the rate of expenditure had declined to 8% of retail sales. An analogous decline in marketing expenditures for individual new products is shown in Table 5-2. The average expenditure rate (as a percentage of sales) declined in Year 2 to about half the Year 1 rate. The only exception to this pattern is the figure for cake mixes, which remains approximately the same throughout the first two years.

Patterns of Sales Growth

Any systematic approach to the planning and evaluation of new products requires some type of sales forecast for a period of two or more years following introduction. In some published discussions of new products, the product life cycle has been suggested as a generalized model of sales trends, both for new *categories* of products and for *individual* new products. A generalized life cycle curve is depicted schematically in Figure 5-1. As shown there, the cycle through which a product is supposed to pass includes four stages: first, an *introductory* stage, in which sales increase slowly; second, a stage of *rapid growth*; third, *maturity*, during which sales change only slightly; and fourth, a stage of *decline*.

This general model, with some modification, appears to describe trends in total sales of food product categories reasonably well.[2] It does not follow, however, that sales of individual new products tend to grow in accordance with the life cycle pattern. Apparently they do *not*, in fact, if the products covered by the survey are representative. Examination of sales histories for the distinctly new

---

[1] Robert D. Buzzell, "Competitive Behavior and Product Life Cycles," in *New Ideas for Successful Marketing*, Proceedings of the 1966 World Congress, American Marketing Association (Chicago, 1966), pp. 46–68.
[2] *Ibid.*, pp. 54–63.

Figure 5-1. Generalized Product Life Cycle Curve

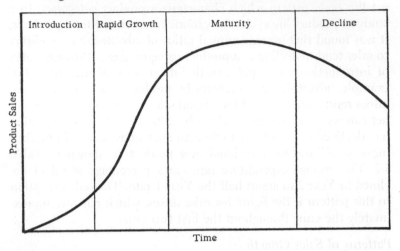

| Introduction | Rapid Growth | Maturity | Decline |

Product Sales

Time

food products introduced between 1954 and 1964 for the first five years following introduction—or up until discontinuance, for those products which were withdrawn in less than five years—reveals three distinct patterns in factory sales volume. These three patterns are depicted schematically in Figure 5-2. One pattern, which has been designated as Steady Growth in the chart, is characteristic of the most successful new products, especially the highly innovative pioneering products. A second pattern, labeled Peak and Decline, involves rising levels of sales volume for two or three years, followed by a decline to a lower level. The decline often reflects the entry of one or more imitative competing products, but even some products which are not faced with such direct rivalry experience a decline in sales after two or three years on the market. In such cases early sales gains are no doubt attributable in large part to product trial by consumers who do not become regular users.

The third pattern shown in Figure 5-2, that of Steady Decline, is characteristic of two groups of products: those that are simply failures, and many of the new versions of variety products such as cake mixes, biscuits, cookies, and crackers, and frozen foods. Often new products in these categories are introduced in the expectation

Figure 5-2. Patterns of Sales Growth and Decline
for Distinctly New Food Products

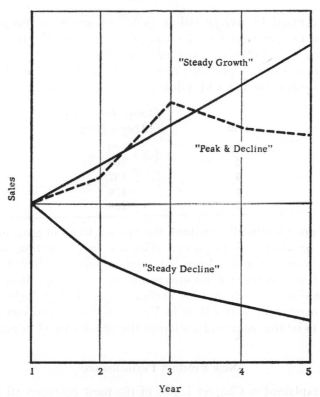

that they will have an extremely limited period of popularity, only to be displaced soon afterward by a subsequent new product of the same company or one of its competitors.

Factory prices of new food products do not change markedly during the first five years following introduction. A median index of average factory price per unit was constructed for 28 products for which a full five years of data were available. This index was practically constant over the five-year period, rising by only 1%. (The Questionnaire instructions called for computation of factory prices *net of deals*, but there was some evidence that not *all* deals were in fact deducted. Hence, the true average factory price per unit probably tends to decline slightly during a product's first five years.)

In contrast to average selling price, average *gross margin per unit* at the processor level typically rises substantially during the first five years following a product's introduction. The median index of gross margin per unit, based on the same 28 products used in computing the index of selling prices, was as follows:

	Median Index of
Year	*Unit Gross Margin*
1	100
2	100
3	107
4	120
5	120

Since price is typically constant, the upward trend in gross margin must be attributed to greater efficiency in production, arising partly from increased volume but, more importantly, from technological and managerial improvements in processing. Since even the products for which sales *declined* typically had higher unit gross margins in Year 5 than in Year 1, process improvement appears to be the main explanation of the upward trend in margins.

New Product Performance

As explained in Chapter 1, one of the most controversial issues related to new products is the extent to which they succeed or fail. In order to make meaningful estimates of success and failure rates, it is necessary both to define what *kinds* of products are to be regarded as new, and to specify what is meant by success. In the survey of food processors, three kinds of measures of product performance were obtained for distinctly new food products. The first and simplest measure is whether a product has been *discontinued* after its introduction; presumably a product is discontinued only if it has failed by one or more standards. A second measure is a *rating* of each product (by management) as (1) highly successful, (2) moderately successful, (3) moderately unsuccessful, or (4) ex-

TABLE 5-3

Discontinuance of Distinctly New Products Introduced in Period 1954–1964

Product Category	Total Products Introduced	After Test Marketing	After Achieving Limited Distribution	After Achieving Full Distribution
Breakfast Cereals—Cold	20	3	1	1
Cake Mixes	14	5	2	3
Frozen Dinners and Specialties	10	1	0	1
Margarine	10	2	3	1
Pet Foods	13	1	0	0
All Product Categories (including those above)	124	27	10	11
Discontinued Products, % of Total Introduced		22%	8%	9%

SOURCE: Responses to Question 9, Schedule B, Appendix.

tremely unsuccessful. A final measure is the difference between cumulative revenue and cumulative direct cost for a product, at various points in time following its introduction. In the sections that follow, each of these measures of performance is applied in turn to the new products covered by the survey.

New Product Discontinuance

Mortality rates for new products at various stages of the development process prior to introduction were given in Chapter 4. Comparable figures for new products discontinued *after* introduction on a regular basis are shown in Table 5-3. Of the 124 products covered by these data, 22% were discontinued after test marketing and an additional 17% were withdrawn following regular introduction.

Why were these products discontinued? Apparently, according to the results shown in Table 5-4, failure in an overwhelming number of instances can be attributed to some form of misjudgment of market conditions.[3] In over three-quarters of the cases, new product discontinuances were attributed to the failure of sales to achieve anticipated levels. It would seem that, in many instances, developers of new products lack sufficient knowledge of what the market will absorb and what the demand will be for the type of product they have available. Poor timing, insufficient marketing effort, competition, and distribution all contributed to unanticipated problems in the marketing of new products.

In a relatively small proportion of cases, difficulties arose from the product itself. In 13% of the cases development and production costs proved higher than expected, while for 15% problems with design and quality *after* introduction forced discontinuance. Finally, in 13% of the cases the product was part of a complete line which was discontinued by a manufacturer. In such instances it is possible that individual products may have been successful, but the failure or inadequate over-all performance of related products led the manufacturer to decide on concentrating his efforts elsewhere.

---

[3] The products covered by Table 5-4 include those discontinued after *test marketing* as well as those discontinued following regular introduction.

TABLE 5-4

Stated Reasons for Discontinuance of Distinctly New Products

Reasons for Discontinuance	% of Products Discontinued after Introduction
MISJUDGED MARKET CONDITIONS:	
Sales did not achieve anticipated levels	77%
Poor timing	21
Insufficient marketing effort	19
Unexpectedly severe competition	15
Failure to achieve adequate distribution	13
PRODUCT DIFFICULTIES:	
Development and production costs higher than anticipated	13
Problem with product design and quality after introduction	15
OTHERS	
Company withdrew from all activities in this area	13
Because of multiple reasons, the figures shown add to:	186%

SOURCE: Based on responses to Question 9b, Schedule B, Appendix, for 48 products discontinued after test marketing or regular introduction.

New Product Performance Ratings

In the preceding section, the term "failure" has been used synonymously with discontinuance of products. It has been assumed, in other words, that discontinued products were failures by some meaningful standard. In this section we examine all products covered in the survey, many of which were *not* discontinued. The categorization of product success used here is that assigned by the manufacturer himself (as judged by responses to Question 8, Schedule B, Appendix). It is not altogether clear, however, by what standards each manufacturer established his judgment of relative success or failure.

Each company was asked to rate each of its distinctly new products as *highly successful, moderately successful, moderately unsuccessful,* or *extremely unsuccessful.* The distribution of responses for 123 products [4] was as follows:

	Number	*Percent*
Highly successful	22	18%
Moderately successful	49	40
Moderately unsuccessful	41	33
Extremely unsuccessful	11	9
	123	100%

Profitability of Distinctly New Products

Because of the high levels of pre-introduction costs, and even more because of the high costs of marketing during the early history of a new product, few distinctly new products begin to make any contribution to overhead costs and profits within a year, or even within two years. This is clearly demonstrated in Table 5-5, which shows average ratios of cumulative contribution to cumulative sales after one, two, and three years of regular distribution. "Cumulative contribution" is defined as the net difference between the cumulative gross profit earned on a product since regular introduction, and the cumulative total of the following costs:

- Pre-introduction research and development and marketing research;
- Total costs for marketing, R&D, and marketing research incurred *since* regular introduction;
- Net "loss" (gross profit minus costs for marketing, R&D, and marketing research) on test marketing prior to large-scale introduction, if any.

No allowance is made in the computation of contribution for fixed costs, even those wholly associated with the individual product (e.g., fixed costs of operating and maintaining special-purpose processing equipment). As a result, a product earning a positive

---

[4] Performance ratings were not assigned for three products because they were introduced shortly before the survey was conducted. One processor failed to supply a performance rating for one product.

TABLE 5-5

Ratios of Cumulative Contribution to Cumulative Sales for Distinctly New Food Products Introduced Between 1954 and 1964, after One, Two, and Three Years of Distribution*

Product Category	End of First Year				End of Second Year				End of Third Year			
	Mean	Median	Range†		Mean	Median	Range†		Mean	Median	Range†	
			Low	High			Low	High			Low	High
Breakfast Cereals—Cold	-14%	-44%	-211%	+44%	- 8%	-16%	-54%	+19%	+ 7%	-13%	- 57%	+15%
Cake Mixes	-25	-17	-117	+36	-19	-14	-140	+32	- 6	- 4	- 25	+ 6
Frozen Dinners and Specialties	-18	- 2	- 80	+10	+ 3	+ 4	0	+10	N.A.	N.A.	N.A.	N.A.
Margarine	- 6	- 6	-478	+33	+ 9	+ 6	-120	+32	+17	+ 8	-120	+34
Pet Foods	-29	-40	-165	+17	- 3	-10	- 40	+23	+ 1	+ 3	- 30	+13
All Product Categories (including the above)	-10%	-13%	-478%	+44%	- 2%	- 2%	-346%	+51%	+ 8%	+ 4%	-120%	+34%
Seven Pioneering Products	-10	- 8	- 38	+14	- 1	+ 1	- 20	+14	+ 8	+ 1	+ 1	+14

* Cumulative contribution is computed by subtracting from the first year's gross profit the following expenses: research and development prior to introduction and during the first year; marketing research prior to introduction and during the first year; net loss on test-marketing operations; and first year marketing expenditures. For detailed definitions of gross profit and of each expense category, see the Questionnaire Guide in the Appendix.

† Minimum and maximum figures. For example, the *least* profitable cold cereal product showed a negative contribution of 211% of first-year sales at the end of its first year.

Sources: Derived from responses to Question 10, Schedule B, Appendix.

contribution may still not be covering its fixed costs, to say nothing of yielding any return on its investment.

Even by this conservative criterion, the financial performance of most new products is poor indeed. At the end of the first year the ratio of cumulative contribution to cumulative sales ranged from −478% to +49%. In none of the categories for which sufficient data permitted separate analysis was the average contribution positive.

Even at the end of the second year the average contribution in three of the five categories was negative. In every case, however, the cumulative contribution was higher at the end of Year 2 than at the end of Year 1. This indicates that *some* current positive contribution is typically earned in the second year, although seldom enough to offset the deficit existing at the end of Year 1. The deficit is typically reduced even further by the end of the third year. By this point in time the average contribution is slightly above the break-even point (i.e., that point at which cumulative contribution reaches or exceeds zero).

The typical profit performance of the pioneering new products was slightly better than the average for *all* distinctly new products. On average, the pioneering products broke even by the end of the second year, and all of them showed positive contributions by the end of the third year. The typical ratio of cumulative contribution to cumulative sales was modest, however.

While some individual products are able to break even fairly soon after introduction, this is uncommon. Table 5-6 shows that, at the end of Year 1, only 30% of all products studied had achieved the break-even level. By the end of Year 2, this figure had risen to 44%, and after Year 3 and Year 4 to 61% and 73%, respectively.

Products within specific categories, however, may experience markedly different patterns of profitability from the average. Table 5-6 reveals, for example, that after *four* years only four of ten cold cereals had yet managed to break even. On the other hand, most margarine and frozen dinners and specialties products had achieved break-even by the end of their second year of full-scale marketing.

On the whole, the findings of this study are quite consistent with those stated by Neil H. Borden some 25 years earlier. Borden found that it is ". . . common experience for new product ven-

Table 5-6

Proportion of Distinctly New Products Achieving Break-Even Levels after One, Two, Three, and Four Years of Distribution, by Product Category*

Product Category	Year 1	Year 2	Year 3	Year 4
Breakfast Cereals—Cold	18%	23%	36%	40%
Frozen Dinners and Specialties	8	33	60	67
Margarine	38	71	71	83
Pet Foods	22	33	40	75
All Product Categories (including those above)	30%	44%	61%	73%

* A product is considered to have achieved break-even if its cumulative dollar contribution equals or exceeds its cumulative dollar cost at a given point in time.

Source: Responses to Question 10, Schedule B, Appendix.

tures to show losses for several years, . . . due in considerable part to the advertising and selling costs incurred." [5]

Product Performance and Pre-Introduction Expenditures

One would expect that if a sponsor of a new product devotes a great deal of effort to its development and testing, chances of success for that product will be increased. Table 5-7 compares average pre-introduction expenditures per product on R&D and marketing research for groups of products, classified according to the ratings of product performance assigned by the sponsoring manufacturers. These figures generally bear out the expectation that performance is related to pre-introductory efforts. R&D expenditures on highly successful products were almost double those on moderately successful and moderately unsuccessful products, while marketing research was two-and-a-half to three times as great. However, the performance of extremely unsuccessful products suggests that there is no guarantee of product success. Average R&D ex-

---

[5] Neil H. Borden, *The Economic Effects of Advertising* (Chicago, Richard D. Irwin, Inc., 194?), p. 858.

penditures on extremely unsuccessful products are higher than for products rated as moderately successful or moderately unsuccessful. (This relationship is circular to some extent, because the processing firms were more likely to regard a product as *extremely* unsuccessful when substantial sums of money had been spent on it.)

TABLE 5-7

Average Pre-Introduction Expenditures on Research & Development and Marketing Research per Product, by Product Performance Rating Category

	Average Expenditure per Product		
Company Success Rating	*R&D*	*Marketing Research*	*No. of Products*
Highly Successful	$95,000	$41,000	22
Moderately Successful	52,000	14,000	43
Moderately Unsuccessful	53,000	18,000	33
Extremely Unsuccessful	78,000	12,000	9

SOURCE: Responses to Questions 8 and 10, Schedule B, Appendix.

Product Performance and Marketing Expenditures

In Table 5-8 the level of marketing expenditures for new products in their first year of regular distribution is compared with the company ratings of product success. For highly successful products, average marketing expenditures represented 31% of sales in the first year. For less successful products (i.e., those rated as moderately successful, moderately unsuccessful, and extremely unsuccessful), the marketing expenditure levels are progressively higher in relation to sales.

It appears that the higher ratio of marketing expenditures to sales on less successful products is primarily attributable to a failure of the new product to achieve anticipated sales levels. Prior to new product introduction, the manufacturer usually has some expectation as to the "natural" sales potential for the product. Based on this expectation, a level of marketing expenditure is established. However, should the manufacturer have substantially *overestimated* sales potential and should the actual resulting sales levels be much smaller, the marketing/sales ratio will be proportionately higher.

In addition to ratio of marketing expenditures to sales, Table 5-8 also compares average first-year dollar marketing expenditures with the company ratings of success. For moderately successful,

TABLE 5-8

Average Marketing Expenditures per Product and Ratios of Marketing Expenditures to Sales, During First Year of Regular Distribution, for Products with Different Performance Ratings

Product Performance Rating	Dollar Expenditures (000)			Ratio to Sales		
	Mean	Low	High	Mean	Low	High
Highly Successful	$2,651	$4	$7,050	33%	3%	93%
Moderately Successful	900	1	5,958	49	1	125
Moderately Unsuccessful	1,113	3	6,293	70	3	309
Extremely Unsuccessful	991	7	3,183	82	21	408

SOURCE: Responses to Questions 8 and 10, Schedule B, Appendix.

moderately unsuccessful, and extremely unsuccessful products the average dollar expenditures in the first year are very similar—approximately $1 million per product. But the marketing/sales ratio for extremely unsuccessful products is *much greater* than that for moderately successful products, and the ratio for moderately unsuccessful products is in turn *greater* than that for moderately successful products. What is implied is that a high dollar expenditure *in itself* is not the primary determinant of product success. The *range* of dollar marketing expenditures, also shown in Table 5-8, tends to support this interpretation. The high figures shown indicate that, among all success rating categories, there was at least one example (and perhaps more) of a very heavily marketed product. While one product was promoted with a marketing expenditure of $7 million and was highly successful, another received a comparable $6 million in marketing expenditures and proved moderately unsuccessful.

Average dollar marketing expenditures on highly successful

TABLE 5-9

Profiles of Distinctly New Food Products: Average Time Spent in Development, Pre-Introduction Expenditures, First-Year Sales, Marketing Expenditures, and Cumulative Contributions

Product Category	Pre-Introduction			First Year of Regular Distribution		
	Total Months Elapsed Between First Development Activity and Achievement of Full Distribution	Cost of R&D	Cost of Marketing Research	Sales	Marketing Expenditures, % Sales	Cumulative Contribution/Cumulative Sales
Breakfast Cereals—Cold	55	$122,000	$60,000	$6,605,000	51%	−14%
Cake Mixes	29	27,000	13,000	938,000	61	−25
Frozen Dinners and Specialties	41	15,000	8,000	416,000	20	−18
Margarine	33	65,000	17,000	6,684,000	30	+ 6
Pet Foods	40	91,000	37,000	3,943,000	49	−29
All Product Categories (including those above)	37	$ 68,000	$26,000	$3,249,000	43%	−10%
Seven Pioneering Products	43	127,000	70,000	11,980,000	41	−10

products were almost three times greater than those for moderately successful products, while the marketing/sales ratio for the two do not differ as greatly. Of further interest here, however, is that the highly successful group included a much greater proportion of highly innovative or pioneering products. For example, the following products, which were either the first or second of their kind to be introduced to the marketplace, were rated as highly successful; a nutritional cereal; a premium margarine; a low-moisture dog food; an extruded dry dog food; a synthetic frozen juice concentrate; a line of boil-in-the-bag frozen vegetable products; and a line of premium frozen vegetable products. All of these products achieved relatively high levels of sales during their first year of distribution. Although dollar expenditures for marketing pioneering products tend to be high, apparently it is not necessary to spend proportionately more to attain these high rates of consumer purchase.

Summary

Some of the key figures presented in Chapters 4 and 5 may now be utilized to provide profiles of new food products in terms of sales, expenditures, and time devoted to development and introduction. Table 5-9 presents profiles for each product category, based on *average* time and cost figures. As should be apparent from the tables in this and the preceding chapter, there is great variation around all these averages. Hence, it is somewhat misleading to speak of any "typical" pattern of research, development, and introduction for new food products. Nevertheless, insofar as average figures represent such common tendencies as there are in the food processing industries, Table 5-9 depicts the situation which confronts the firms in those industries.

The profiles of new food products clearly support the generalization that product innovation is costly, risky, and time-consuming. The costs and risks involved lead, in turn, to some potentially important economic effects. Some of these effects are explored in the following chapter.

CHAPTER 6

The Effects of Product Innovation

THE INFORMATION summarized in Chapters 3, 4, and 5 provides a partial basis for examining some of the *effects* of product innovation in food processing on the various groups involved in the production, distribution, and consumption of new food products. In this chapter we discuss some of the major effects of product innovation on each of these groups; i.e., its effects on consumers, on food processors, on distributors, and on the economy as a whole. We do not, however, attempt to weigh all these effects in a balance and arrive at any final verdict on the desirability of new products for any of these groups or for society at large. A balance sheet on product innovation includes both assets and liabilities, both benefits and costs. Any balancing of the benefits against the costs necessarily involves value judgments. For example, what is increased product variety worth to consumers? Is the value of variety sufficient to offset the costs incurred to provide variety? Reasonable men differ in their appraisals of this and of other trade-offs between benefits and costs. Our own opinion, based on an *a priori* belief in the effectiveness of what appears to be a workable competitive market for processed foods, is that the benefits of new products greatly exceed the associated costs. This opinion rests in part on our appraisal of the specific benefits of new products for each group, as summarized in the sections which follow.

Effects on Consumers

Adam Smith pointed out long ago that "consumption is the sole end and purpose of all production." [1] As a modern corollary

---

[1] Adam Smith, *The Wealth of Nations* (New York, Modern Library, Cannan edition, 1937), p. 625.

to this axiom, increased consumer satisfaction is the sole end and purpose of all product innovation—in food processing or in any other industry. It follows that the most important factors to consider, in any evaluation of product innovation by food processors, are its effects on the consuming public.

The potential benefits of new food products to consumers include increased choice, reductions in preparation and purchasing time, improvements in flavor, and improvements in nutrition. The costs which may be incurred in attaining these benefits include (sometimes) higher prices and a more complex buying task. *Some* of these benefits and costs can be measured, at least in part, on the basis of the information presented in Chapters 3, 4, and 5 and of the results of other studies. Others cannot be quantified readily, if at all. For example, whether a given product change represents an improvement in *flavor* is a purely subjective question. Even the nutritional effects of product innovation are very difficult to assess; there is no clear-cut evidence of the benefits of polyunsaturated oils, for example. Even if there were, the net benefit to a given consumer would depend on the rest of his diet and other factors.

Because of the inherent difficulties of measuring consumer benefits and costs, even in crude terms, only a partial assessment of the effects of product innovation can be attempted here.

Product Variety

It is perfectly clear that one major effect of product innovation during the post-World War II era has been to broaden the variety of choice available to consumers. It is a matter of common observation that American food stores offer larger assortments of products than those typically available in other countries. It has also been generally recognized that the number of different products stocked by an average food store increased substantially during the 1950's and 1960's. According to one trade source, "the average food store assortment" increased from 4,000 items in 1950 to 5,800 in 1959, and further to 6,900 in 1964.[2] This increase in the

---

[2] *Progressive Grocer*, "Facts in Grocery Distribution," 1956 edition, and issue of April 1965, p. 101.

typical food store's *total* assortment reflects at least two major concurrent trends: the diversification of food stores into nonfood merchandise lines and the effects of product innovation within various food product categories.

To what extent has the assortment of processed food products increased because of product innovation? Comparison of the warehouse catalogs of Grand Valley Markets in 1954 and 1964 gives an indication of the effects of innovation on variety. The data for 21 processed food categories are summarized in Table 6-1. This table shows the number of items stocked in each category in 1954, the number of items added and dropped between 1954 and 1964, and the resulting changes in product assortments for each product category. Items added during the 10-year period are classified into two groups: items of new *types* which were introduced after 1954 and items of types already stocked in 1954. For example, within the cold breakfast cereal category, 62 items were added between 1954 and 1964; of these, 53 were regular and presweetened cereals (types carried by Grand Valley prior to 1954), while 9 were *nutritional* cereals, a new type added during the decade.

The figures in Table 6-1 clearly reflect the constant change which has characterized food marketing during the 1950's and 1960's. For the 21 categories combined, the number of items added between 1954 and 1964 (1,106) was three-and-a-half times as great as the *total* number stocked at the beginning of the period (320). This influx of new items was offset in part, however, by the discontinuance of 556 items. The net result of all this activity was an increase in the combined product assortment from 320 items to 870.

Of the 1,106 items added by Grand Valley Markets between 1954 and 1964, slightly under 10% (91) were of new types not carried at the beginning of the period. The total figure includes 232 frozen dinner and specialty items, however, none of which were classified as new types because of ambiguities in the definition of types within this category (see Chapter 3). Consequently, it seems likely that somewhat more than 10% of all items added by Grand Valley during the 10-year period were products of new types introduced after 1954. This figure may be compared with the estimates given in Chapter 3, that new types of products introduced after 1954 represented about 7% of total 1964 *sales volume* at Grand Valley Markets, while all new items accounted for approximately 65% of 1964 sales volume.

The rate of change in product assortments varied considerably among product categories, as shown in Table 6-1. Only one category, soluble coffee, experienced a net decrease in the number of items stocked; one other category, evaporated and condensed milk, remained static. In two-thirds of the product categories (14 of 21) the number of items stocked increased by 100% or more. Two categories—cake mixes and frozen dinners and specialties—accounted for more than 40% of the total number of items added. As pointed out in earlier discussions, these product categories and certain others such as biscuits, cookies, and crackers, may be termed variety categories. The vast majority of new products introduced in the variety categories, even those which meet the definition of distinctly new products, are relatively minor variations or improvements in existing products in terms of ingredients, form, and processing technology. The same is true, to a somewhat lesser degree, of frozen vegetables, frozen juice concentrates, packaged dessert mixes, and pourable salad dressings.

Critics of the food processing industry often minimize the value of increased variety, labeling it as "wasteful proliferation." The fact that consumers have accepted so many new food products suggests, however, that consumers place considerable value on added product variety. The fact that so many *other* new food products have been rejected and withdrawn from the market suggest that consumers have, and use, the freedom of choice to decide *which kinds* of new products they want.

Food Costs

In popular discussions of new food products, primary attention has been focused on the more dramatic innovations such as frozen dinners and boil-in-the-bag frozen vegetables. These and similar products incorporate so-called built-in maid service, in that they are more nearly ready to serve than most conventional food products. Not only are products with such high degrees of built-in maid service new in dramatic, visible ways, but they typically cost considerably more than fresh or home-prepared equivalents—a

TABLE 6-1

GRAND VALLEY MARKETS

Number of Items Stocked in Selected Processed Food Categories: 1954 and 1964

Product Category	Stocked in 1954	Items Added			Dropped 1954–1964	Net Change 1954–1964	Stocked in 1964
		Existing Types	New Types	Total			
Breakfast Cereals—Cold	32	53	9	62	27	+ 35	67
Breakfast Cereals—Hot	17	8	0	8	6	+ 2	19
Cake Mixes	39	207	0	207	138	+ 69	108
Dehydrated Potatoes	1	8	13	21	9	+ 12	13
Evaporated and Condensed Milk	8	5	0	5	5	0	8
Flour—All-Purpose	11	8	4	12	2	+ 10	21
Frozen Dinners and Specialties	15	N.A.	N.A.	232	115	+117	132
Frozen Juice Concentrates	15	53	1	54	27	+ 27	42
Frozen Vegetables	33	109	16	125	51	+ 74	107
Liquid Dietary Foods	0	—	11	11	0	+ 11	11

Margarine	9	16	7	23	12	+11	20
Nonfat Dry Milk	4	12	0	12	8	+4	8
Packaged Dessert Mixes	48	63	0	63	37	+26	74
Packaged Rice Products	6	9	8	17	3	+14	20
Peanut Butter	7	13	0	13	3	+10	17
Pet Foods	23	95	3	98	37	+61	84
Powdered Coffee Creamers	1	1	5	6	2	+4	5
Salad Dressing—Nonpourable	15	10	0	10	6	+4	19
Salad Dressing—Pourable	5	63	14	77	36	+41	46
Soluble Coffee	19	20	0	20	21	−1	18
Vegetable Shortening and Cooking Oil	12	30	0	30	11	+19	31
Totals (21 categories)	320	783	91	1,106*	556	+550	870

* Total of 1,106 items added includes 232 frozen dinner and specialty items which were not classified into existing or new types (see text).

SOURCE: Warehouse withdrawal records, Grand Valley Markets.

frozen complete chicken dinner may cost twice as much per serving, for example, as a similar dinner prepared at home from fresh and canned ingredients. Because of the apparent differences in cost for *some* new food products, there has been a widespread tendency to assume that new foods *in general* are more expensive than established products.

In an article written in 1960, Bainbridge Crist pointed out that:

> What the industry calls convenience foods has become an easy target . . . it seems quite logical to pin much of the blame for increased food marketing costs on these newer items which have grown so rapidly in popularity during the postwar years.[3]

Because both prices paid by consumers and the prices received by farmers are perennially popular political issues, it is important to determine the effects of product innovation on prices insofar as this can be done.

This study did not deal specifically with comparative costs of new *versus* established processed foods. A very useful study of this subject has been conducted, however, by Marshall E. Miller and Philip P. Dwoskin of the Economic Research Service, U.S. Department of Agriculture.[4] Since cost is one of the major issues associated with product innovation, some of the findings of the USDA study are summarized briefly below.

Miller and Dwoskin studied the comparative costs *per serving* of convenience foods and fresh or home-prepared foods. Many of the convenience foods included in the study were not especially *new*—for example, ready-to-serve baked goods, tea bags, and canned vegetables. Others, however, were products first introduced after World War II, such as frozen orange juice concentrate, soluble coffee, frozen dinners, and cake mixes. Average retail prices for these products, and for equivalent dishes or meals prepared at home, were estimated by obtaining monthly price

---

[3] Bainbridge Crist, "Myths About Convenience Food Costs," *Journal of Marketing*, April 1960, p. 49.

[4] *Comparative Costs to Consumers of Convenience Foods and Home Prepared Foods*, Marketing Research Report No. 609, U.S. Department of Agriculture, Economic Research Service, Marketing Economics Division (Washington, 1963).

data over the course of a year in leading supermarkets in four major metropolitan areas. These prices were converted to a per-serving basis, and estimates were also made of time requirements for preparation.

The main conclusion of the Miller and Dwoskin study was that *the total consumer expenditure on convenience foods is actually less* (by about 2%) *than the expenditure that would be required for equivalent amounts of home-prepared foods.* Although the per-serving costs of most convenience products (116 out of 158) were higher than for their home-prepared counterparts, consumers purchased much greater amounts of the cost-reducing convenience foods. In the computation of the comparative expenditure figures, each product was weighted by its estimated volume of sales.

The conclusion that total expenditures for convenience foods were lower than for equivalent amounts of home-prepared foods was based on data for both old and new convenience products. The same conclusion holds, however, if the comparison is restricted to products introduced after World War II. Cost and expenditure estimates for these types of products, taken from the Miller and Dwoskin study, are reproduced in Table 6-2. As shown in the table, two relatively new products—frozen orange juice concentrate and soluble coffee—were substantially less expensive on a per-serving basis than their home-prepared equivalents. Both of these products are bought in large volume. The result is that, in terms of dollar expenditure, savings on orange juice concentrate and soluble coffee far more than offset the added costs of the other relatively low-volume products. It should be pointed out that this conclusion does *not* necessarily imply that consumers *spend* less than they would have spent if the newer types of products had not been introduced at all. If total consumption of a group of product categories (such as beverages) has been increased, then aggregate dollar expenditures may well be higher on account of the introduction of new products.

One other conclusion of the Miller and Dwoskin study is relevant to an assessment of the effects of innovation: namely, the reduction in food *preparation time* associated with many new processed foods. For each of the convenience foods which cost

TABLE 6-2

Estimated Costs Per Serving and Dollar Expenditures by Consumers on Selected Convenience Food Products and Home-Prepared Equivalents

(Convenience Products Introduced since 1946)

Convenience Product	Cost per Serving		Consumer Expenditures, per $100 of Food Purchases	
	Convenience Product	Home-Prepared Equivalent	Convenience Product	Home-Prepared Equivalent
COST REDUCING:				
Cake Mixes				
devil's food	$.0249	$.0359	$ .035	$ .050
yellow	.0204	.0238	.024	.029
Frozen Orange Juice Concentrate	.0371	.0757	.682	1.391
Soluble Coffee	.0074*	.0145	1.000	1.959

Cost Increasing:				
Dehydrated Potatoes				
mashed	.0345	.0225	.047	.032
other†	.0440	.0729	.072	.041
Frozen Beef Dinner	.6061	.3192	.059	.032
Frozen Beef Pie	.2496	.1654	.047	.031
Frozen Chicken Pie	.2512	.1985	.094	.073
Frozen Turkey Dinner	.6516	.2477	.106	.040
Instant Tea	.0113	.0055	.058	.028
Pie Mixes				
cherry	.0727	.0674	.070	.064
coconut	.1002	.0713	.018	.013
Precooked Rice	.0308	.0117	.094	.036
Total			$2.406	$3.819

* Average cost per serving based on different amounts per cup recommended by different manufacturers.
† Averages of scalloped and au gratin potatoes.

Source: Based on estimates in *Comparative Costs to Consumers of Convenience Foods and Home-Prepared Foods*, Marketing Research Report No. 609, Economic Research Service, Marketing Economics Department, U.S. Department of Agriculture (Washington, 1963), Tables 3, 4, 26, 30, 31, 33, 34, and 40.

more than its home-prepared equivalent, Miller and Dwoskin estimated the time savings provided by the convenience product. This time saving was then divided into the cost difference between convenience and home-prepared products, to derive an equivalent "cost of work time saved by using convenience foods." For example, the cost differential between dehydrated and home-prepared mashed potatoes was $0.011 per serving, while the time saved by using the dehydrated version was estimated at 2.5 minutes. On the basis of these figures it was estimated that the equivalent cost of work time saved—i.e., of the built-in maid service—was $0.26 per hour.[5] Cost-per-hour estimates of this type were made for all the cost-*increasing* convenience foods. These equivalent costs varied widely from product to product—from $0.04 per hour for frozen French fried potatoes to $3.07 for frozen poundcake—and the average was about $0.60 per hour.

Miller and Dwoskin conclude that the added costs of processing inherent in most convenience products:

> . . . are apparently cancelled out in the aggregate by a reduction in the cost of transportation and handling, or by the substitution of one service for another. . . . To achieve lower food costs by the use of convenience foods, the individual consumer needs to be—and apparently usually is—selective in choosing from the items available.[6]

This conclusion lends further support to the belief that consumers generally exercise freedom of choice in an intelligent manner in appraising the new food products which are available to them.

Effects on Food Processing Firms

Among the major groups concerned with product innovation in foods, none has as great a direct financial stake in new products as the processing firms. While the success or failure of a single new product has only a small effect on the overall welfare of a distributor, a consumer, or even the economy at large, the for-

---

[5] Ibid., p. 62.
[6] Ibid., p. 5.

tunes of even the biggest food processing firms depend importantly on market acceptance or rejection of a relatively small number of new products.

The episode of Jason Merrill, presented in Chapter 1, illustrates some of the major objectives which food processors pursue in their new product activities. The principal incentive to processors to undertake product development programs is the belief that new products will yield increased sales and profits. There is no doubt that *some* companies succeed in attaining these goals; it is equally clear that some other companies fail. On the whole, how great a contribution do new products make to increased sales and profits? This question is explored in the paragraphs immediately following.

Sales Growth

At any given point in time a large food processing company's product line consists of an assortment of items of varying degrees of maturity—a mix of old and new products. For products in the *older* segments of the mix, the usual pattern of sales is one of stability, with relatively gradual increases or decreases in volume.

From an overall corporate viewpoint, then, only modest growth can usually be expected to stem from the older segment of the product mix. The focal point of growth activities, therefore, falls in the area of new product development and introduction.

For the case of *distinctly new products* the extent to which product innovation is related to overall corporate growth is examined in Table 6-3. For 11 companies the growth in total sales in 20 product categories between 1958 and 1964 was determined; on this basis, six companies were classified as having high overall growth, and the remaining five as having moderate overall growth. Among the high growth companies an average of almost 73% of the 1958-1964 sales increase was accounted for by distinctly new products introduced in the period under study. The remaining sales growth was presumably attributable to the introduction of line extensions and to an increase (or decline) in the sales of older products introduced prior to 1958. For moderate growth companies only 47% of the overall increase was attributable to the introduction of distinctly new products.

TABLE 6-3

Growth in Total Corporate Sales Accounted for by Introduction of Distinctly New Products, 20 Processed Food Categories: 1958–1964

| | | 1964 Sales of Distinctly New Products Introduced since 1958 | |
Company	*% Increase in Total Sales, 1958–1964*	*% of Total Sales Increase, 1958–1964*	*% of 1964 Sales*
HIGH GROWTH COMPANIES:			
A	84.3%	64.4%	31.1%
B	59.1	51.2	19.0
C	37.5	70.4	19.2
D	36.8	33.2	8.9
E	35.0	116.2	30.2
F	34.4	96.8	26.0
Weighted Average, 6 High Growth Companies	43.3%	72.7%	22.0%
MODERATE GROWTH COMPANIES:			
G	22.6%	34.0%	7.7%
H	20.0	69.8	11.6
I	19.4	19.7	3.2
J	16.1	37.9	6.1
K	7.9	20.6	1.7
Weighted Average, 5 Moderate Growth Companies	20.3%	47.3%	8.0%

SOURCES: Responses to Question 10, Schedule B, Appendix; Question 2, Schedule C, Appendix; and A.C. Nielsen Company data.

There is apparently a direct relationship between the level of product innovation (as exemplified by the introduction of distinctly new products) and the extent of overall corporate growth. In almost every case, high levels of new product activity are associated with correspondingly high rates of growth in total company sales. At least with respect to corporate growth from within, product innovation would seem to be the most important single source of growth for large food processing companies.

The importance of new products to food processors is further demonstrated by the figures in the last column of Table 6-3. These figures are estimates of the proportions of each company's *total* 1964 sales volume accounted for by distinctly new products introduced since 1958. Among the high growth companies new products represented more than 20% of total sales on average. For two of the firms new products accounted for nearly a third of total sales. With one exception, new products represented less than 10% of total sales for the moderate growth companies.

In principle, there remains an alternative means of achieving growth, that of acquisition. In many cases, to purchase a brand can be less expensive, and certainly less time-consuming, than to develop one. In practice, however, this avenue of growth is severely restricted for most large processors. Existing levels of concentration in many grocery categories are already regarded by antitrust authorities as high, and further acquisitions almost invariably encounter close scrutiny and opposition by federal government agencies. Studies by the National Commission on Food Marketing indicate that since World War II acquisition has been a much less important source of growth for food processors than internal expansion.[7]

In the future it seems likely that the obstacles to growth through acquisition will become even greater. If this prognosis is correct, then the relative attractiveness of internal growth will increase, and processors are likely to devote even greater resources to research and development, to marketing research, and to intro-

---

[7] National Commission on Food Marketing, *Studies of Organization and Competition in Grocery Manufacturing*, Technical Study No. 6 (Washington, Government Printing Office, 1966), pp. 23–26.

ductory marketing for new products than they do at present. The data in Table 6-3 suggests that these efforts can be successful.

Profits

The data presented in Chapter 5 show that it is unusual for a new food product to make any contribution to its fixed costs of production and distribution, much less to earn a net profit, during the first two or three years after introduction. Large food processors do not expect any profits from an individual new product during this introductory phase. But they *do* expect to increase total company profits *eventually* as a result of product innovation. It is generally expected that a product will yield the highest rate of profit of its entire history during the years just following the introductory phase, when the product still retains some degree of distinctiveness.

To what extent are food processors' expectations of increased total profits realized? The data obtained in the survey of food processing companies do not provide an adequate basis for a meaningful answer to this question because they do not cover a sufficiently long period of time. Overall effects of new products on profits were estimated for the same 11 firms which were examined in terms of sales increases in Table 6-3. For these companies *total cumulative dollar contributions* were calculated for *all* distinctly new products introduced during the period 1958 to 1964. The results indicate that new products have *not* generally contributed significantly to company profits over the 6-year period. Only 4 of the 11 companies received *any* positive contribution to fixed costs and profits from their distinctly new products. For each of the other 7 firms the total gross revenue from new products during the 7-year period was insufficient to cover the total direct costs associated with these products.

Overall profits for a 7-year period do not, however, constitute a fair test of the impact of new products. As indicated in Chapter 5, new food products do not achieve break-even levels, in terms of cumulative costs and revenues, until the third or fourth year following introduction (see Table 5-6). Hence, it is not surprising that a company's overall set of new products introduced at varying points during a 7-year time span should not yet have yielded a positive return.

One additional comment on the subject of profits may be in order. The interviews which were conducted with food processors indicated that the methods currently used for evaluating the expected profitability of a new product leave much to be desired. Quite apart from the inherent difficulties of estimating sales volume during periods three, five, or more years in the future, most of the processors apparently do not treat the costs and investments associated with new products in a systematic fashion. The most common criterion for new product evaluation is the estimated pay-out period, i.e., the length of time required for the profit contributions earned on a product to recoup the costs incurred prior to and during its introduction. No allowance is typically made for foregone profits, that is, the yields which might have been earned on whatever investments are available as alternative uses for the funds devoted to new product research, development, and introduction. Since the time lags between these expenditures and the eventual receipt of the revenues which serve to pay out new product efforts are usually significant, it seems desirable to make appropriate allowance for the returns which might have been earned in the interim.

Effects on Food Distributors

The analysis of warehouse withdrawal data for Grand Valley Markets, summarized in Chapter 3, provides a basis for evaluating some of the effects of new food products on food distributing institutions. Two types of effects are of special interest: the growing workload involved in appraising new products and the impact of new products on distributors' margins. Although the data presented in this study apply only to this one food chain, it is believed that other distributors have experienced generally similar results during the 1950's and 1960's.

The New Product Workload

The data presented in Chapter 3 make it perfectly clear that the amount of work required to evaluate new products which are offered to food chains and wholesalers, and to review existing product assortments, has increased substantially during the 1950's and 1960's. As shown in Table 6-4, the average number of new items *added* from period to period in the 21 product categories studied between 1960 and 1964 was approximately one and two-thirds times as great as in 1954–1958. The number of items dropped

TABLE 6-4

GRAND VALLEY MARKETS

Changes in Numbers of Items and Brands Stocked, 21-Category Totals: 1956–1964

	NEW ITEMS Change since Preceding Period			NEW BRANDS Change since Preceding Period		
Year	*Number Added*	*Number Dropped*	*Net Change*	*Number Added*	*Number Dropped*	*Net Change*
1956	184	38	+146	47	10	+37
1958	156	88	+ 68	27	17	+10
1960	188	81	+107	40	19	+21
1962	299	141	+158	54	32	+22
1964	279	208	+ 71	52	37	+15
5-period average	221	111	+110	44	23	+21

SOURCE: Warehouse withdrawal records, Grand Valley Markets.

increased by an even greater proportion from an average of slightly over 60 per 2-year period in 1956–1958 to an average of over 170 in 1962–1964. These figures represent only a portion of the *total* workload created by product innovation, since only a fraction of the new items offered to a chain or wholesaler are actually adopted. According to executives of the Grand Valley chain, for every new item added by the company during recent years, 10 to 12 others were considered and rejected.

How do food distributors cope with the problems of evaluating prospective new products? In most chains and wholesalers, *buying committees* are used to make "add and drop" decisions.

Buying committees were relatively uncommon prior to 1950, but by the early 1960's this organizational arrangement had come into widespread use.[8] Typically a buying committee consists of the several departmental buying and merchandising personnel, the top merchandising executive(s), and possibly the sales and advertising managers of a company. As described in the example of Carl Zimmerman in Chapter 1, the buyers responsible for various departments perform a screening function prior to the meetings of the committee. Perhaps a fourth to a third of all new items offered to buyers are considered by the buying committee.

The factors considered by buying committees in appraising new products offered to them can be inferred from an examination of the standardized "new item offer" forms which most distributors employ. These forms usually include information on such factors as: [9]

1. Suggested retail price
2. Cost, quantity discounts, and cash discounts offered; freight costs to distributor, if any
3. Advertising and promotional allowances offered, if any; special introductory allowances
4. Advertising planned by supplier
5. Comparable items currently stocked
6. Competitive stores currently stocking the new item
7. Method of shipment, delivery time, etc.

Buying committee discussions, based on these types of information, usually deal with potential sales of the proposed new item, effects of its adoption on sales of comparable items, and so on. Most buying committees do *not*, however, employ any systematic techniques for estimating potential sales and profits of new items. Nor do the buyers or the committees in most firms have any staff personnel available to prepare such estimates.

In view of the rapid increases in the number of new items

---

[8] Howard L. Gordon, "How Important is the Chain Store Buying Committee?", *Journal of Marketing*, pp. 55–60.

[9] An example is reproduced in Malcolm P. McNair, William Applebaum, and Walter J. Salmon, *Cases in Food Distribution* (Homewood, Illinois, Richard D. Irwin, 1964), p. 180.

offered to chains and in the number added and dropped, it appears that more systematic methods for appraising new products might be desirable. There is clearly some limit on the number of products which can be appraised with any degree of certainty by a committee, operating in an essentially informal manner. Moreover, the increasing scarcity of shelf space in food stores, relative to the variety of products available, seems to call for more refined estimates of "performance" for both new and existing products. The concept of direct product profit has been developed as a basis for evaluating products, and it seems logical to use some profit measure of this kind in estimating the net effect of adding a given new item.[10] To do this, it will be necessary for distributors to develop more formal and more systematic procedures than those currently used by most companies.

Effects on Gross Margins

During the 1950's and 1960's average gross margins of food distributors increased substantially. For example, the composite gross margin for food retailers participating in the annual studies of operating results conducted by the Super Market Institute rose from 17.4% of sales in 1954 to 19.8% in 1963.[11] Many factors contributed to this increase; the most important ones appear to have been higher advertising and promotion expenses (including trading stamps) and rising wage rates.[12] Some observers have suggested that new products have also contributed to the increase in gross margins. If processors find it necessary to offer wider

---

[10] The concept of direct product profit is presented in the *McKinsey-General Foods Study: The Economics of Food Distributors* (New York, McKinsey & Company, 1963). For some illustrative applications, see Robert D. Buzzell, Walter J. Salmon, and Richard F. Vancil, *Product Profitability Measurement and Merchandising Decisions: A Pilot Study in Retail Food Stores* (Boston, Division of Research, Harvard Business School, 1965).

[11] National Commission on Food Marketing, *Excerpts from Super Market Institute Figure Exchange Reports, 1954–1964*, Supplement No. 1 to Technical Report No. 7, *Organization and Competition in Food Retailing* (Washington, Government Printing Office, 1966).

[12] "Margins: Why Are They Rising?", *Progressive Grocer*, April 1966, p. 218. See also *Food from Farmer to Consumer*, Report of the National Commission on Food Marketing (Washington, Government Printing Office, 1966).

margins on new items as an inducement to their adoption, the replacement of older products by newer ones might lead to an increase in distributors' overall gross margins.

The warehouse withdrawal records of Grand Valley Markets included both costs and retail prices for all items stocked, and these figures were used to determine gross margins on new *vs.* established items in each of the 21 product categories studied. Comparative gross margins in 1964 on items added in 1964, and on items stocked since 1954, are summarized in Table 6-5. The pattern presented by these data is certainly a mixed one. In 10 of the 19 product categories in which new items were added in 1964, the gross margin percentage for the new items is higher than the category average; in 9 cases it is lower than average. There does not appear to be any *systematic* tendency toward higher margins on newer products.

Even though new products do not *themselves* necessarily carry higher gross margins than established products, the introduction of so many new items during the 1950's and 1960's has undoubtedly contributed to the upward trend in distributors' overall margins. Product assortments have expanded greatly, as shown in Table 6-1. These increases in assortment create greater workloads and added costs for distributors in terms of higher inventories in relation to sales, more complex problems of inventory control, warehousing, delivery, shelf replenishment, and checkout activities. This additional workload is presumably *one* of the factors which has contributed to higher overall labor costs, space costs, and interest charges. Apparently, however, distributors have in effect spread the cost increases throughout their total product lines, and have *not* sought or obtained higher margins on new products on the basis of their greater *incremental* costs of operation.

Aggregate Economic Effects

Since everyone in the economy is necessarily a consumer of foods, the effects of product innovation discussed in the first section of this chapter may also be considered as aggregate economic effects. In other words, if increased choice and reduced

TABLE 6-5

GRAND VALLEY MARKETS

Gross Margin as a Percentage of Sales in 1964 for New Items, Old Items, and All Items: Selected Product Categories

	Gross Margin Percent		
Product Category	Items Stocked since 1954	Items Added in 1964	All Items in Category
Breakfast Cereals—Cold	17.6%	18.6%	18.3%
Breakfast Cereals—Hot	21.6	22.5	21.8
Cake Mixes	18.2	18.3	18.7
Dehydrated Potatoes	20.2	22.7	22.1
Evaporated and Condensed Milk	16.0	——*	16.3
Flour—All-Purpose	17.6	26.7	18.5
Frozen Dinners and Specialties	47.4	28.1	31.9
Frozen Juice Concentrates	33.0	29.1	28.2
Frozen Vegetables	37.5	31.6	34.9
Margarine	27.9	19.2	23.6
Nonfat Dry Milk	23.9	19.8	19.6
Packaged Dessert Mixes	16.7	17.2	17.1
Packaged Rice Products	23.1	21.3	21.7
Peanut Butter	18.3	18.6	18.7
Pet Foods	20.7	21.7	21.8
Powdered Coffee Creamers	——†	22.8	23.0
Salad Dressings—Nonpourable	21.5	21.3	21.6
Salad Dressings—Pourable and Dry	23.0	22.2	22.0
Soluble Coffee	14.6	14.2	13.8
Vegetable Shortening and Cooking Oil	21.6	28.6	24.3

* No items added in 1964.
† No items stocked in 1954 still carried in 1964.

SOURCE: Warehouse withdrawal records, Grand Valley Markets.

costs are beneficial to the individual consumer, they are *ipso facto* beneficial to the economy. Beyond this, we wish to examine some economic effects of product innovation which are not so apparent at the level of the individual household. In this section we examine briefly the effects of new food products on total marketing expenditures for processed foods and on concentration within certain food product categories.

Effects on Concentration

In its report to the President, the National Commission on Food Marketing devoted considerable attention to the subject of concentration in food processing. One conclusion of the Commission's report was that there is ". . . high concentration in some segments of the food industry, and growing concentration in much of it." [13] A high degree of concentration is generally regarded by economists as undesirable because it ". . . weakens competition as a self-regulating device by means of which the business activities of firms are directed toward the welfare of the public at large." [14]

The issue of concentration in food processing is related to product innovation because the vast majority of new products have been introduced by large companies. Insofar as these newer products succeed in displacing older ones, they may serve as one of the means by which dominant firms in an industry increase their market shares. It is, therefore, relevant to ask whether concentration has increased more—or decreased less—in those product categories characterized by a high degree of innovation than in less innovative product categories.

Trends in concentration within 11 product categories for which the relevant data were available are shown in Table 6-6. The measure of concentration used in this table is the combined market share of the three leading processing companies in each product category. Of the 11 categories, 6 experienced relatively high rates of new product introduction between 1954 and 1964,

---

[13] *Food from Farmer to Consumer*, p. 93.
[14] Ibid., p. 94.

while 5 were characterized by relatively low new product activity (cf. Table 3-22, Chapter 3).

The data suggest *some* relationship between the extent of product innovation and trends in concentration levels, but the

TABLE 6-6

Trends in Concentration Within Specified Product Categories, Related to Extent of Product Innovation

Product Category and Extent of Innovation	Combined Market Share of 3 Leading Processors		
	1954	1959	1964
HIGH INNOVATION:			
Breakfast Cereals—Cold	84%	84%	84%
Dehydrated Potatoes	N.A.	61	59
Dog Food—Semimoist	45	50	60
Packaged Rice Products	19	20	20
Powdered Coffee Creamers	100*	100*	99†
Salad Dressings—Pourable and Dry	57	62	67
LOW INNOVATION:			
Breakfast Cereals—Hot	N.A.	71	74
Evaporated Milk	73	73	64
Packaged Desserts	90	93	90
Peanut Butter	53	58	54
Vegetable Shortening	68	60	62

* One company.
† Three companies.
SOURCE: Based on A.C. Nielsen Company estimates of market shares.

data are too limited to support any clear-cut conclusion. In two of the highly innovative categories—dry dog food and pourable salad dressings—concentration increased significantly. In three other innovative categories, concentration was essentially unchanged, while in one—powdered coffee creamers—concentration declined. Among the five less innovative product categories, the share of the market accounted for by the three leading companies declined in two cases and was unchanged in three others.

Effects on Marketing Expenditures

Marketing expenditures—especially expenditures for advertising, selling, and other forms of promotion—constitute an important part of the total marketing margin [15] for food products. For this reason, the level of processors' marketing expenditures and the trend in such expenditures have a significant bearing on the economic performance of the food processing industries. In its report to the President, the National Commission on Food Marketing stated that:

> The substantial costs built into the price of food as a result of various forms of selling effort—advertising, sales promotion, expensive packaging, salesmen—are an important form of *inefficiency* in the food industry. . . . The power of such selling efforts reduces the role of price competition and thus moderates pressures on the industry to cut costs of other functions.[16]

Not only did the Commission thus express concern over present levels of marketing costs, but it also predicted that in the future ". . . increased emphasis on most forms of selling effort will offset some of the effects of more efficient distribution on costs and prices." [17]

The data collected in the survey of food processors indicate that aggregate marketing expenditures are, in fact, rising. Combined sales and marketing expenditures for 17 large processing firms are summarized in Table 6-7. The marketing expenditures data in this table include all costs of media advertising, sales force compensation and expenses, and sales promotion such as displays, premiums, and samples.

As shown in Table 6-7, the ratio of marketing expenditures to sales increased gradually but steadily throughout the period 1954–1964. By 1964 the total costs of advertising, selling, and promotion amounted to over 11% of net sales. Even this figure is

---

[15] The term "marketing margin" is used conventionally to designate the difference between the price paid by consumers for a product and the prices received by farmers for its raw ingredients, including all processing costs.
[16] *Food from Farmer to Consumer*, p. 99.
[17] Loc. cit.

an understatement, because the figures shown in Table 6-7 include both sales and marketing expenditures for the extensive *fresh* food operations of one very large company. If this company is excluded from the figures, the combined ratio of marketing expenditures to sales was 10.4% in 1954 and 13.6% in 1964.[18]

TABLE 6-7

Sales and Marketing Expenditures, 17 Large Food Processing Firms: Selected Years, 1954–1964

		Marketing Expenditures*	
	Net Sales	Amount	
Year	*(000)*	*(000)*	% of Sales
1954	$4,974,237	$401,102	8.06%
1956	5,215,453	467,118	8.96
1958	5,600,947	517,275	9.24
1960	5,636,042	603,128	10.70
1962	6,005,665	636,169	10.59
1964	6,579,563	752,998	11.44

* Includes expenditures for media advertising, personal selling, and sales promotion.

SOURCE: Derived from responses to survey, Schedule A, Question 1 (see Appendix).

Several factors have contributed to the rising level of marketing expenditures by food processors. For one thing, the use of *television* as an advertising medium increased substantially during the 1950's and 1960's as television receiver ownership expanded, more stations went on the air, and new facilities (especially color) became available.

Another contributing factor was increased *costs* for some advertising media. The net effect of media cost changes is not, however, entirely clear. *Published* prices per unit of time or space have increased for virtually all major media, but this is offset in part by increased audiences. For example, the cost of network

---

[18] Dollar amounts cannot be given without violating the agreement under which the data were obtained.

television per hour, *per thousand homes* in the audience, actually declined by more than 15% from 1954 to 1964. Even after allowance for audience increases, however, average costs of most types of media increased by 20% to 30% during this period.[19]

Comparisons of *published* media prices are of limited value in an analysis of advertising expenditures by large firms, because so many types of discounts are usually available to companies that advertise on a large scale. There is no reliable information available on the extent of such discounts, or on changes in the magnitude of discounts from one time period to another. For this reason, any conclusion regarding the effect of media cost changes on advertising expenditure levels is speculative at best. Our speculation is that, on balance, *effective* media costs for reaching an audience of a given size increased only slightly for large food processors during the period in question. If this was the case, then the upward trend in marketing expenditures must be explained on the basis of factors other than increases in advertising media costs.

Product innovation contributes to increased marketing expenditures in two ways. First, as pointed out in Chapter 5, when a new product *category* is developed and introduced, marketing expenditures are typically very high in relation to sales during the first few years—the introductory stage of the category's life cycle. During this period sales of the product typically grow slowly, so that costs cannot be spread over a large volume of output. Moreover, an extensive educational task must be performed in order to achieve widespread consumer acceptance. Later, when (and if) the product attains widespread use and when imitators compete increasingly on a price basis, the rate of marketing expenditure tends to decline.

The net impact of higher marketing costs for new product categories on *total* marketing costs depends, of course, on the proportion of total food sales represented by such categories. As shown in Chapter 3, new *types* of food products (introduced since 1962) represented only about 2.5% of total processed food sales in

---

[19] Based on estimates published in *Printers' Ink,* issues of October 30, 1959; January 10, 1964; January 8, 1965.

1964. It is apparent that no matter how high the introductory marketing expenditures were for these new types of products, their impact on total industry marketing expenditures must be relatively slight.

A more important source of increased marketing expenditures is the introduction of new products *within* existing product categories. As shown in Table 5-2, average marketing expenditures for distinctly new products represent 43% of sales during the first year of distribution and 24% of sales during the second year of distribution. These figures are more or less comparable with the overall average marketing-to-sales ratio of 13.6% previously given for large processing firms. Consequently, if the proportion of a firm's total sales accounted for by distinctly new products increases, a corresponding increase in the overall ratio of marketing expenditures to sales can be expected.

The impact of distinctly new products on marketing expenditures by large processors, at least for the period 1958–1964, can be estimated from the data obtained in the processor survey.[20] In 1964 sales of distinctly new products introduced in 1963 or 1964 accounted for about 6% of total sales for the 17 large firms which supplied information. Marketing expenditures represented approximately 33% of sales for these new products, or about 2% of the companies' *overall* sales. This level of marketing expenditure on new products is much higher than the corresponding figure for 1958, which is estimated to have been about 1% of total company sales. These are, admittedly, rough approximations. The implication of the estimated increase in new product marketing expenditures is that *about half of the total increase in large food processors' marketing expenditures since 1958 is attributable to higher rates of marketing effort devoted to distinctly new products.* Although the calculation is a rough one, it does seem likely that the order of magnitude in the end result is correct. Thus, it seems

---

[20] The overall effect cannot be measured directly, because information was obtained for *total* company food sales and marketing expenditures and for new product sales and expenditures only in selected product *categories* (see Schedule A, Survey Questionnaire, Appendix). In order to put these two sets of figures on a comparable basis it is necessary to estimate the companies' total sales and expenditures *in the categories covered by the study.*

highly probable that a substantial portion of the overall increase in marketing expenditures can be explained by the costs of introduction for an increased number of new products.

One independent piece of evidence tends to corroborate the estimate given in the preceding paragraph. For ready-to-eat cereals we were able to obtain data on sales and advertising expenditures for (1) all brands and (2) brands introduced to the market in

TABLE 6-8

Retail Sales and Advertising Expenditures, Ready-to-Eat Breakfast Cereals: 1959 and 1964

	1959	*1964*	*Increase*
Retail Sales (000)	$401,072	$577,389	+44%
Advertising Expenditures (000)	63,207	78,452	+24
Estimated Index of Advertising Media Costs	100	113	+13
Advertising Expenditures, Adjusted for Media Cost Changes	63,207	69,427	+10
Advertising Expenditures for Products in First Two Years of Distribution	9,050	13,639	+51
Adjusted for Media Cost Changes	9,050	12,070	+33

SOURCE: Based on A. C. Nielsen Company sales data and on advertising expenditure estimates provided by a major cereal producer.

various years between 1959 and 1964. These data are summarized in Table 6-8. As shown there, total retail sales of ready-to-eat cereals increased by 44% between 1959 and 1964. The increase in total advertising expenditures was about half as great, at 24%. About half of this increase can be attributed to higher media costs.[21] If allowance is made for media cost increases, the in-

---

[21] The index of advertising media costs for cereal advertisers was developed in connection with a study of product life cycles for food products conducted by the authors and submitted to the National Commission on Food Marketing, under the sponsorship of the Grocery Manufacturers of America. The increase shown here is not believed to be inconsistent with the conclusion stated earlier that cost increases have not contributed significantly to the overall growth in *marketing* expenditures for *all food products* between 1954 and 1964.

crease in cereal advertising expenditures was about 10%, or $6.2 million. During the same period, advertising expenditures for *new* cereals—those introduced to the market within the preceding two years—increased by 50% in current dollars, or by 33% after adjustment for cost changes. The *net* increase in new product advertising, after adjustment, was $3.0 million, or just about half of the total increase in cereal advertising expenditures.

The foregoing estimates, crude as they are, suggest that higher rates of new product introduction have been a major contributing factor to the increases in advertising and other marketing expenditures which have occurred in the 1950's and 1960's. Even if an adjustment could somehow be made for this factor, marketing expenditures have still increased on account of other factors, presumably including more intense competition and the introduction of product line extensions and product improvements. But the growth in marketing expenditures, above and beyond that attributable to new products, is substantially less than that reflected in estimates of total industry expenditures.

CHAPTER 7

Conclusions and Implications

As STATED in Chapter 1, the broad purpose of this study was to provide a basic description, definition, and measurement of product innovation in the food processing industries during the post-World War II period. Statistical information about new food products was obtained from three primary sources: the warehouse withdrawal records of a large food chain, a survey of food processors' practices in new product development and introduction, and A. C. Nielsen Company estimates of retail sales on a national basis. The findings of the study have been presented in Chapters 3 through 6. In this chapter the major conclusions are summarized, and some of their implications for executives of food processing and distributing companies and for governmental officials are explored briefly.

What Is a New Product?

The term new product is ambiguous because both words—new and product—are subject to varying interpretation. Lack of a uniform definition has been a major source of confusion over such issues as the extent of product innovation and the new product failure rate. As suggested by the discussion in Chapter 2, there is no single correct definition of a new product which can serve equally well for all purposes. Two *sets* of definitions were suggested, one based on the food processor's point of view and one based on that of the food distributor. For the processor, it is useful to distinguish three mutually exclusive classes of new products: *product improvements, product line extensions,* and *distinctly new products.* The last of these three classes may be subdivided, in turn, into pioneering new products (those basically different from *any* product previously on the market); and products new to the individual processor but essentially similar to products of other companies. The distinction between pioneering new products and other distinctly new products is clear enough in principle, but hard to apply in practice. For purposes of analysis, pioneering products were defined so as to include both the *first* and *second* brand of a new product to be introduced. The second brand was included on the ground that in most cases the second entrant has commenced development effort long before the first brand is actually introduced.

From the distributor's viewpoint, three classes of new products were also identified: *new items, new brands,* and *new types* of products. These categories are *not* mutually exclusive.

The Extent of Product Innovation

The analysis of warehouse withdrawal records for the Grand Valley Markets food chain, summarized in Chapter 3, indicated that in each year since 1954 new items introduced during the preceding two years represented between 20% and 25% on total annual sales volume in the 21 product categories studied. The share of sales accounted for by new items has changed very little since 1954. New *brands* represented 10% to 12% of annual sales during the early part of the period, declining to between 6% and 8% of annual sales in 1962–1964. The fraction of total sales attributable to new *types* of products rose from about 1% of sales in 1956 to 2.5% in 1964.

For the 10-year period as a whole, new items (introduced since 1954) represented almost two-thirds of 1964 sales; new brands about one-third; and new types of products, around 7%.

The magnitude of new product introduction may also be judged by the *number* of new items introduced. Between 1954 and 1964 the total number of items stocked by Grand Valley increased from 320 to 870, reflecting the addition of 1,106 items and the discontinuance of 556 (Table 6-1). Of the total number of new items added, about 10% were items of new types first stocked after 1954.

Thus, both in terms of sales volume and in terms of numbers

of items, new types of products represented about one-tenth of total new item introductions during the 10-year period.

New Products and Sales Growth

A major objective of food processors in introducing new products, and a major inducement for distributors to stock them, is that of achieving sales growth. The information presented in Chapters 3 and 6 indicates that new products do, in fact, contribute significantly to increased sales. Comparison of sales increases for Grand Valley Markets, in product categories characterized by differing rates of new product introduction, shows that high growth categories are also the ones in which new items and new types account for the highest proportions of total sales (Table 3-22). The effects on overall sales of *all* food products are not clear, because of the complex patterns of substitution among and within product categories.

The relationship between product innovation and growth is also clear at the processor level. Among high growth processing firms, distinctly new products introduced since 1958 accounted for an average of 20% of 1964 sales. For companies that achieved lower rates of growth during the same period, new products accounted for only 8% of 1964 sales (Table 6-3).

The Sources of Product Innovation

Prior to World War II most new food products were conceived and developed by individual inventors or by small companies. During the post-World War II period there has been a marked increase in the importance of large processing companies as a source of product innovation. As shown in Table 4-2, all the new types of products introduced since 1960 in the 21 product categories studied have come from large food processors. Some, at least, of these recent new products represent significant departures from existing food products. Semimoist pet foods, instant blending flour, freeze-dry soluble coffee, and synthetic orange juice concentrate are all significant innovations, and all were introduced between 1960 and 1964.

The importance of large firms in the development of new food products is also indicated by the fact that very few smaller companies responded to the survey of processors' activities (Chapter 1), and that those who were contacted by telephone said that they had little or nothing to report in the way of research and development. Studies by the National Science Foundation and by McGraw-Hill Publishing Company also show that large firms account for the bulk of R&D spending in the food industries (see Table 4-3).

Table 4-3 also shows that the increasing importance of large processors as a source of new products during the late 1950's and early 1960's coincided with a substantial rise in the rate of R&D expenditure by the large firms. Even the largest food processing companies' R&D expenditures are small, in relation to sales volume, compared with those of firms in such other industries as ethical drugs, electronics, and chemicals. But the rate of research and development effort by the larger processors has been much higher since the mid-1950's than at any time in the past, and this increased effort has contributed to a higher rate of new product introduction.

The increasing importance of large firms in the development of new food products parallels a similar trend in other industries. Studies of the relationship between innovation and company size have shown that large firms usually have distinct advantages in new product development because of (1) economies of scale in R&D, (2) the ability to spread risks, and (3) the opportunity to exploit the results of R&D on a larger scale through access to national markets.[1] All these advantages seem to apply to food processing as well as to other industries, although scale economies in R&D are clearly less important. Some of the newer techniques of food preservation and processing, such as freeze-dehydration and irradiation, are more complex than conventional technologies, and this may contribute to more significant scale economies in food processing R&D in the future. At present, scale economies

---

[1] See, for example, *Economic Concentration:* Hearings Before the Subcommittee on Antitrust and Monopoly, Committee on the Judiciary, U.S. Senate, 89th Cong., Part 3: *Concentration, Invention, and Innovation* (Washington, Government Printing Office, 1965), p. 1200.

in *marketing* appear to be substantially more important than those associated with research, development, or processing. The average marketing expenditure for a distinctly new product during its first year of regular distribution of $1.4 million is many times greater than the average R&D cost per product of $68,000 (Tables 5-2 and 5-10). Thus, the inability to support an appropriate introductory advertising campaign, and/or to achieve adequate distribution in retail stores in a reasonable period of time, is undoubtedly a more significant disadvantage for the smaller firm than any lack of technical resources for new product development.

The Product Development Process

In a large food processing company the activities involved in developing, testing, and introducing a new product usually follow a common basic sequence, starting with research directed toward a specific product concept or idea and moving through product testing to test marketing and finally to introduction, often initially on a limited scale. There is wide variation in the time devoted to the steps in the product development process and in the costs of carrying out these steps, as shown in Tables 4-6 and 4-7. Average expenditures per product, for all product categories combined, amounted to $68,000 for research and development, $26,000 for marketing research, and $248,000 for test marketing (Tables 4-7 and 4-8).

From the standpoint of development time and costs, it is useful to distinguish between variety food product categories and other classes of products. The variety categories, including frozen dinners and specialties, biscuits, cookies and crackers, and cake mixes, are characterized by relatively low time and cost requirements. Even distinctly new products within these categories are usually similar to existing products in form, ingredients, and other characteristics.

Our attempts to obtain information about product development activities revealed a general lack of systematic records on the subject. Only one processing firm had compiled a reasonably comprehensive history of its own past new product experiences, and none had any idea how its own performance compared with that of other companies. The lack of historical information and standards almost surely makes it more difficult to plan and control present and future new product development activities. Some of the larger food processors, however, were experimenting with the application of so-called network analysis techniques (PERT and Critical Path Method) to product development activities. Use of these techniques requires estimation of expected time and cost requirements for each step in the product development process. Hence, if the newer techniques appear to be useful for planning and control purposes, it can be expected that better and more complete records will be kept in the future. The questionnaire used in this study (see Appendix) suggests some of the kinds of information that it may be useful to record, although much more detail will be needed for network analysis methods.

New Product Introduction

Marketing expenditures for new food products are extremely high during the first year of regular distribution, averaging 43% of sales (Table 5-2). This rate of expenditure in relation to sales is more than three times as great as the average rate of marketing expenditure for all processed food products, as shown in Table 6-7. Marketing expenditures per product decline during the second year of distribution, both in dollars and even more markedly in relation to sales.

Because marketing expenditures are so high during the early years of distribution for a new product, the increase in the rate of new product introduction which has occurred during the 1950's and 1960's has, in turn, contributed to a higher overall level of marketing expenditures by food processors. A rough estimate presented in Chapter 6 indicates that about half of the increase in processors' marketing expenditures, in relation to sales, can be attributed to the higher proportion of total sales accounted for by new products.

Sales of a new food product after its introduction tend to follow one of three basic patterns: steady growth, growth and decline, or steady decline. The most successful new products, including all the pioneering products covered by this study, experience steady growth. Products that are faced with direct competitive substitutes within three or four years often experience declines after an initial period of growth. The steady decline pattern is characteristic of many "variety" products as well as of unsuccessful products in other categories.

None of the products covered by this study followed the so-called product life cycle pattern of sales growth, which seems to be descriptive of trends in sales of a product *category* rather than of an individual product.

The diversity of patterns in sales growth and decline, together with the high degree of risk associated with new food products, suggests the importance of improving current methods of sales forecasting. Sales forecasts are required as a basis for evaluating the profitability of a proposed new product at various points prior to its introduction, commencing with the decision to allocate funds to product research. Our interviews with executives and marketing research personnel in processing firms indicated that current forecasting methods leave much to be desired. Considerable effort has been devoted to devising better methods of sales forecasting, but much more needs to be done.

New Product Success and Failure

Estimates of the rate of new product failure given in popular discussions of the subject are almost invariably exaggerated. The actual rate of failure depends, of course, on what products are included in the base against which a failure rate is computed, as well as on the criteria employed to identify failures.

Among the 127 distinctly new food products covered by this study, 39% were discontinued either after test marketing or after regular introduction. A similar proportion, 42%, were classified by their sponsors as either extremely unsuccessful or moderately unsuccessful. A third criterion of product performance is the length of time required for the contributions to profit earned from a product to offset its development and introduction costs. By this criterion, 44% of the 127 products had failed to break even after two years of regular distribution. Thus, if a single figure must be used to characterize the rate of failure among new processed food products, it appears that approximately 40% should be classed as failures.

A comparison of product failure rates with various tangible characteristics of new products revealed little in the way of common determinants of success. Not surprisingly, all the pioneering new products were successful; all these products involved substantial, visible differences from existing products in taste, form, preservation, or other physical attributes. Average expenditures per product for research and development and for marketing research were somewhat higher for highly successful products than for those with lower performance ratings, as shown in Table 5-7.

A comparison of average marketing expenditures per product for new products achieving differing degrees of success (Table 5-8) shows that a high rate of promotional spending does not guarantee success. The average expenditure per product was considerably higher for highly successful products than for others, but this expenditure is probably influenced to a considerable extent by early feedback as to the product's sales performance. There was at least one very heavily promoted product in each of the performance rating groups, indicating that the deficiencies of a poor product cannot be overcome simply by large-scale promotion.

The Effects of New Products

The introduction of new food products has provided a much greater variety for consumers, as shown in Table 6-1. Although a majority of new convenience products—which account for a high proportion of all new foods—are more costly than home-prepared equivalents, some are substantially less expensive. Consumers tend to buy much greater amounts of the cost-reducing products, so that in the aggregate new products have tended to reduce food costs to the consumer.

The food processing firms that have achieved the greatest increases in sales volume during the 1950's and 1960's are also the ones for which new products are most important. Thus, innovation appears to have been used successfully as a basis for corporate growth. The effects on processors' overall profits are not clear. As suggested in Chapter 6, better methods are needed for appraising the profit effects of new products, present and proposed.

New products have created a substantial and growing workload for food distributors, as shown in Table 6-4. The buying committee method for evaluating product additions and discontinuances does not seem adequate for the burden that is being placed on it, unless it is supplemented by staff assistance and/or a more effective use of data processing equipment.

Finally, with respect to the economy as a whole, product innovation in food processing has contributed to higher levels of marketing expenditures. The rate of marketing expenditure tends to decline over a period of time following a product's introduction, however, and eventually price competition tends to become predominant. Although many economists feel that direct price competition would be desirable at an earlier point after a new product is introduced, it would be a mistake to neglect the important functions performed by introductory marketing efforts. Only after consumers are fully aware of a product and its performance characteristics, and only after the product has become reasonably standardized in its basic form, can meaningful price competition emerge. There seems to be no reason to alter the conclusion offered 25 years ago by Professor Neil H. Borden, who stated that

> . . . the imitator who enters the market and makes his bid for business on a price basis performs a significant social service. . . . he helps to bring low costs and low prices in established industries. On the other hand, the innovator should be given credit for the important social service he performs. He develops improved products and builds for them a public acceptance and demand. . . . he paves the way for imitators.[2]

---

[2] Neil H. Borden, *The Economic Effects of Advertising* (Chicago, Richard D. Irwin, Inc., 1942), pp. 858–859.

APPENDIX

Questionnaire Forms Used in
Survey of Food Processing Companies

CONFIDENTIAL   SCHEDULE A
                                    COMPANY INFORMATION

*For definitions and instructions, see
accompanying Questionnaire Guide.*

Name of company _____

Address _____

1.   **SALES AND MARKETING EXPENDITURE INFORMATION**

Please provide the following data for *calendar years* 1954-1964 or
for your company's fiscal years most nearly corresponding thereto
(if fiscal years, please indicate beginning dates).

Year (1)	Net Domestic Sales of Consumer Food Products (2)	Media Advertising (3)	Sales Force Compensation (4)	Sales Promotion (5)	Marketing Research (6)	Total Research & Development (7)	If total reported in Col. (7) includes basic technological research conducted by or on behalf of your Co., please enter check(✓) here. (8)
1954							
1955							
1956							
1957							
1958							
1959							
1960							
1961							
1962							
1963							
1964							

Explanation of fiscal year basis: _____.

Schedule A - page 1

INDICATE BY CHECKING (✓) IN ONE OR MORE COLUMNS IF:

Product Category		Company *now markets*, or *did market* at some time since Jan. 1, 1954, products in this category *under company's own brand names*, and:		Company has engaged in some new product development work during past or all of period since Jan. 1, 1954 which *did not result, or has not yet resulted*, in new products being introduced to the market.	Company now manufactures, or has manufactured at some time since Jan. 1, 1954, products in this category to be sold *under wholesalers' retailers' or other distributors' brand names*.
		Distinctly new products have been introduced since Jan. 1, 1954.	Line extensions or product improvements have been made since Jan. 1, 1954, regardless of introduction date of original product.		
(1)		**(2)**	**(3)**	**(4)**	**(5)**
Biscuits, cookies and crackers	(1)				
Breakfast cereals - cold	(2)				
Breakfast cereals - hot	(3)				
Cake mixes	(4)				
Canned Vegetables	(5)				
Dehydrated potatoes	(6)				
Dog food — dry and canned	(7)				
Evaporated milk (including condensed milk)	(8)				
Flour — all purpose type	(9)				
Frozen dinners and specialties	(10)				
Frozen juice concentrates	(11)				
Frozen vegetables	(12)				
Margarine	(13)				
Peanut butter	(14)				
Packaged dessert mixes (flavored gelatines and puddings)	(15)				
Packaged rice products	(16)				
Powdered coffee creamers	(17)				
Processed cheese	(18)				
Refrigerated and frozen dough products	(19)				
Salad dressing — liquid (pourable) and dry types	(20)				
Salad dressing — non-pourable type	(21)				
Vegetable shortening and cooking oil	(22)				
FURTHER ACTION REQUIRED ⟶		**COMPLETE SEPARATE COPY OF SCHEDULE B FOR EACH NEW PRODUCT IN EACH OF THOSE CATEGORIES CHECKED IN COLUMN 2**	**COMPLETE SEPARATE COPY OF SCHEDULE C FOR EACH CATEGORY CHECKED IN COLUMN 3 AND/OR COLUMN 4.**		**FOR CATEGORIES CHECKED IN COLUMN (5), NO FURTHER ACTION IS REQUIRED**

Schedule A - page 2

CONFIDENTIAL

SCHEDULE B

DISTINCTLY NEW PRODUCTS INTRO-
DUCED SINCE JAN. 1, 1954

_____

(Name of Company)

*For definitions and instructions, see
accompanying Questionnaire Guide.*

Schedule B should be completed by the person (s) most directly
familiar with the history of the product for which information
is given. Please complete a *separate schedule for each distinctly new product*
introduced since Jan. 1, 1954. Information on *line extensions and
product improvements* should be given in Schedule C. Complete Schedule
B for all products marketed or test marketed for the first time
during the period since Jan. 1, 1954.

1	2	3

4	5	6

1. Name of new product:_____

2. Brief description_____

_____

7	8

3. Product category (see list in Schedule A)_____

4. For your company, what was the source of the idea for this new product?(Check one
    or more):

9-1 _____ new product survey research conducted by your company, or by an external
                agency or firm on behalf of your company

9-2 _____ open-end discussions with consumers conducted by your company or by an
                external agency or firm on behalf of your company

9-3 _____ company research and development laboratories

9-4 _____ company sales personnel

9-5 _____ marketing research involving other products, either conducted by your
                company or by an external agency or firm on behalf of your company.

9-6 _____ advertising agency

9-7 _____ trade customers (distributors, retailers, et cetera)

9-8 _____ suppliers

9-9 _____ trade magazines or reports

Schedule B - page 1

10-1 _____ consumer magazines or reports

10-2 _____ universities or non-profit research organizations

10-3 _____ outside consultants or market research firms

10-4 _____ federal government or its agencies

10-5 _____ competing companies

10-6 _____ other sources (specify)_____

10-7 _____ _____

10-8 _____ _____

10-9 _____ _____

5. For each of the following steps in the development of this new product, please
   give the   *approximate dates of the beginning of each step,*   or if unable to give
   dates, the *time elapsed between the beginning of each step:*

	Beginning Date (month and year)	If unable to give dates, please estimate time elapsed between beginning of each step

a. Product research and development (as a recognized activity in budgets, schedules, etc.)

b. Product testing other than informal testing by company employees--if any. (if none, show "none".)

     (months or years)

c. Test marketing, if any. (if none, show "none".)

d. Introduction on limited area basis.

e. Full-scale introduction throughout company's marketing area

11 12
□ □

13 14
□ □

15 16
□ □

17 18
□ □

19 20
□ □

21 22
□ □

Schedule B - page 2

6a. The questions that follow hereafter explain various attributes which *might* be
characteristic of a new product, and ask you to indicate if the attribute in
question is descriptive of your particular new product which is the subject
of this Schedule. For example, one of the questions is:

> "Did this new product permit a reduction in the
> amount of time required for a housewife to pre-
> pare a dish or meal?"

In each case, the changes, improvements or reductions referred to are to be
assessed *relative* to products' existing in the category prior to introduction of
this new product. (For examples, see Questionnaire Guide.)

The questions are arranged in three groups:

Group #1: Processing and Packaging
Group #2: Storage and Transportation Methods
Group #3: Preparation and Use by the Consumer

For each question in each group, please answer **YES** or **NO** (if applicable)
for this new product:

Group #1 - Processing and Packaging

		Yes	No	Not Applicable
		(1 or A)	*(2)*	*(3)*
(1)	Did this new product involve any change(s) in basic raw material ingredients?	23 ___	___	___
(2)	Did it involve any change(s) in other ingredients?	24 ___	___	___
(3)	Did it involve any change(s) in processing methods and/or equipment?	25 ___	___	___
(4)	Did it involve any change(s) in packaging materials and/or methods?	26 ___	___	___
(5)	Did it permit more efficient use of byproducts from existing processing operations?	27 ___	___	___
(6)	Did this product permit processing at a lower direct cost than would otherwise be required for an equivalent amount of a similar product?	28 ___	___	___
(7)	Did it involve a change in manner of dispensing from the package?	29 ___	___	___

Group #2 - Storage and Transportation Methods

(8)	Did this new product permit any reduction in the amount of space required for storage in the home and/or on the shelf?	30 ___	___	___

Schedule B - page 3

		Yes	No	Not Applicable
		(1 or A)	(2)	(3)

(9) Did it permit storage in the home and/or by the trade for a longer period of time?

31 ___ ___   ___

(10) Did it permit (or require) a change in the manner of storage in the home and/or by the trade?

32 ___ ___   ___

(11) Did it involve a change in weight and/or volume which resulted in lower shipping costs?

33 ___ ___   ___

(12) Did it provide greater availability to an otherwise seasonal product or ingredient?

34 ___ ___   ___

(13) Did it involve a fundamental change in form (e.g. from liquid to solid, from fresh to dehydrated, etc.)?

35 ___ ___   ___

Group #3 - Preparation and Use by the Consumer

(14) Did this new product permit a reduction in the amount of time required for a housewife to prepare a dish or meal?

36 ___ ___   ___

(15) Did it permit (or require) a change in the method or technique of preparation?

37 ___ ___   ___

(16) Did it permit the housewife to prepare a dish or meal in a manner less cumbersome or messy (for example, lesser number of pots and utensils; pots and utensils less dirty or "sticky")?

38 ___ ___   ___

(17) Did its preparation involve less waste of raw material than would have otherwise been experienced in preparing this dish for a household of average size (4-5 persons)?

39 ___ ___   ___

(18) Did it utilize ingredients which are not generally conveniently available to consumers (for example, rarely used spices, sauces or herbs)?

40 ___ ___   ___

(19) Did it provide greater dependability in the preparation of a dish or meal?

41 ___ ___   ___

(20) Did it permit greater uniformity of quality in a dish or meal?

42 ___ ___   ___

Schedule B - page 4

		Yes	No	Not Applicable
		(1 or A)	*(2)*	*(3)*

(21) Did it result in a dish or meal whose method of preparation, without this new product, was sufficiently complex that housewives would not normally attempt its preparation, or in a dish or meal whose method of preparation housewives would generally be unfamiliar with? *43* ___ ___ ___

(22) Did it permit or facilitate any changes in the circumstances of use by consumers (for example, new occasions for eating; snacks versus meals, etc.)? *44* ___ ___ ___

(23) Did it provide significant new nutritional or dietary benefits to the consumer? *45* ___ ___ ___

(24) Did it involve a change in taste which was discernable to consumers? *46* ___ ___ ___

(25) Did it involve a change in texture which was discernable to consumers? *47* ___ ___ ___

(26) Did it involve a change in appearance which was discernable to consumers? *48* ___ ___ ___

(27) Was it generally offered at a lower retail price? *49* ___ ___ ___

6b. Please explain any other significant innovative attributes of this new product which are not described by your responses to the previous questions in 6a.

_____ *50*

_____ *51*

_____ *52*

_____ *53*

_____ *54*

_____ *55*

_____ *56*

_____ *57*

_____ *58*

Schedule B - page 5

7.   For these statements to which you have responded "yes" in question 6a,
or for any statements you may have added in question 6b, please **CIRCLE**
the three or four attributes which describe the *most important innovative features
upon which the marketing strategy for this product was based.* **(INDICATE BY CIRCLING THE
APPROPRIATE CHECK MARKS IN QUESTION 6a AND/OR BY CIRCLING THE APPRO-
PRIATE STATEMENTS IN QUESTION 6b.)**

8.   Was this product regarded by your company as:

59-1 _____   highly successful

59-2 _____   moderately successful

59-3 _____   moderately unsuccessful   } check one

59-4 _____   extremely unsuccessful

9.   a.) Was this product   *discontinued*   at some point subsequent to its introduction?

60-1 _____   Yes

60-2 _____   No

b.) If "YES", why was the product discontinued? (check (✓) one or more):

61-1 _____   sales did not achieve anticipated levels.

Schedule B - page 6

61-2 _____ difficulties with product design, quality or other product defects were encountered after introduction of the product.

61-3 _____ development and production costs were higher than anticipated.

61-4 _____ poor timing; market conditions changed between the time of product conception and to its subsequent introduction to the marketplace.

61-5 _____ competitors with similar or related existing products took severe defensive measures in response to the introduction of the new product (e.g. substantial price cutting, unusually high advertising and promotional expenditures, etc.).

61-6 _____ competitors(s) introduced similar or related new products which achieved unanticipated success.

61-7 _____ insufficient marketing effort was allocated to support introduction of the new product.

61-8 _____ failure to achieve adequate distribution for the new product.

61-9 _____ other reasons; specify:_____

61-0 _____

61-x _____

61-y _____

_____

_____

_____

_____

Schedule B - page 7

**PLEASE CONSULT THE QUESTIONNAIRE GUIDE FOR DEFINITION OF THE FIGURES
REQUESTED BELOW**

10a. For the full period *prior to introduction*   of this new product (either on
a test market, limited area, or full distribution throughout company's
marketing area, basis) please indicate the following *for this product:*

Total expenditures on research
and development *prior to introduction:*

_____
(dollars)

Total expenditures on marketing research *prior to introduction:*

_____
(dollars)

Schedule B - page 8

10b.   *From date of introduction* to present, please complete the following table *for this product:*

For the   *first two years after date of introduction,*   provide data by *quarterly* periods.   *However,* if the last quarterly period shown on this basis is *not* the final quarter in your company's fiscal year, please provide additional quarterly data up to the beginning of the next full fiscal year.

QUARTERLY periods for first two years after introduction (1)		Total Factory Sales (units)	Total Net Factory Sales ($)	Gross Profit ($)	Marketing Expenditures ($)	Product Research and Development Expenditures ($)	Marketing Research Expenditures ($)	For each period indicate by checking (✓) if distribution was less than throughout company's full marketing area
Months	Year	(2)	(3)	(4)	(5)	(6)	(7)	(8)

For periods *after* the final period shown in the above table, and up to the present, please provide data on an *annual* basis only:

(10b to be continued)

Schedule B - page 9

10b continued

Year (1)	Total Factory Sales (units) (2)	Total Net Factory Sales ($) (3)	Gross Profit ($) (4)	Marketing Expenditures ($) (5)	Product Research and Development Expenditures ($) (6)	Marketing Research Expenditures ($) (7)	For each period indicate by checking (✓) if distribution was less than throughout company's full marketing area (8)

NOTES

FOR THE FIGURES YOU HAVE SHOWN IN THE ABOVE TABLES, PLEASE INDICATE THE FOLLOWING:

(1) If the figure for the first quarterly period shown is less than a full 3-month period, please so indicate:_____

(2) If the final annual figure shown is less than a full 12-month period, please so indicate:_____

(3) Please specify the nature of "units" reported in column (2)_____

(4) Total Net Factory Sales, as you have reported here, is (check one):

　　　____ net of all price deals, or

　　　____ net of some price deals, or

　　　____ not net of price deals　　　(For explanation, see Questionnaire Guide)

Schedule B - page 10

CONFIDENTIAL

**SCHEDULE C
LINE EXTENSIONS, PRODUCT
IMPROVEMENTS AND NEW PROD-
UCT DEVELOPMENT, SINCE JAN.
I, 1954.**

*For definitions and instructions see
Questionnaire Guide*

———————————————
Name of Company

Please complete one copy of this schedule for   *each product category*   in which you
have:

- Introduced line extensions since Jan. 1, 1954, regardless of the
  date of introduction of the original product,

  and/or

- Made product improvements since Jan. 1, 1954, regardless of the
  date of introduction of the original product,

  and/or

- Engaged in some new product development work during part or all of
  the period since Jan. 1; 1954 which did not result, or has not yet
  resulted, in distinctly new products being introduced to the market.

Schedule C - page 1

1. Product·category (see list in Schedule A):_____ ▬

2. If you have introduced line extensions in this product category since
    Jan. 1, 1954, please complete the following table *for the category as a whole:*

Year	Number of line extensions introduced	Number of previous extensions withdrawn	Total sales volume of all products in this category marketed by your company (dollars)	Percentage (on dollar basis) of your total category sales accounted for by line extensions introduced since Jan. 1, 1954
(1)	(2)	(3)	(4)	(5)
1954				
1955				
1956				
1957				
1958				
1959				
1960				
1961				
1962				
1963				
1964				

NOTE: If the year (column 1) shown above is a fiscal year which does not correspond
       to the calendar year, please explain its basis:_____

3. If you have made improvements to products in this category since Jan. 1, 1954, please complete the following table *for each product* to which improvements have been made since Jan. 1, 1954 (if you require additional space, use reverse side of this page):

Product (1)	Date of Improvement (year) (2)	Brief Description of Improvement (3)

Schedule C - page 3

4. If you have introduced line extensions, or made improvements to products, in this category since January 1, 1954, please complete the following table for the category as a whole:

Year (1)	Total Product Research and Development Expenditures on line extensions and product improvements (2)	Total Marketing Research Expenditures on line extensions and product improvements (3)
1954		
1955		
1956		
1957		
1958		
1959		
1960		
1961		
1962		
1963		
1964		

Schedule C - page 4

mpany who might be involved in completing these questionnaires. Should
quire additional copies, please contact us immediately at the telephone
r shown below.

Guide is intended to be both definitional and illustrative. Definitions
provided for many terms which might otherwise be subject to varying inter-
etation in different company settings (for example, "net factory sales").
lustrations are intended to supplement definitional statements, particularly
here such definitions do not lend themselves to a quantifiable or precise
form (for example, what are illustrations of a "line extension"?).

5a. If, at some time since Jan. 1, 1954, your company has engaged in the
development of new products in this category, but such new product
development did *not* result in products being introduced to the marketplace, please complete the following table *for the category as a whole:*

Year (1)	Number of distinctly new products for which funds were expended on development, but for which further development was terminated, after:		Expenditures on development of distinctly new products, which were not introduced to the marketplace, on:	
	Product Research and Development (no. of products) (2)	Product Testing (no. of products) (3)	Product Research and Development (dollars) (4)	Marketing Research (dollars) (5)
1954				
1955				
1956				
1957				
1958				
1959				
1960				
1961				
1962				
1963				
1964				

5b. If you are *currently* developing new products in this category, but such new products have not yet been introduced to the marketplace, please complete the following table *for the category as a whole:*

Number of distinctly new products current-ly under development	Expenditures to date on the development of these products		Total anticipated expen-ditures on development of these products in the re-mainder of your company's current fiscal year.	
	Product Research & Develop-ment (dollars)	Marketing Research (dollars)	Product Research & Develop-ment (dollars)	Marketing Research (dollars)

Schedule C - page 6

CONFIDENTIAL

194

**SURVEY OF NEW PRODUCT RESEARCH, DE...
MARKETING ACTIVITIES OF FOOD PROCESS...
1954-1964**

QUESTIONNAIRE GUIDE

This Questionnaire Guide has been prepared to assist you in com... accompanying questionnaires, and to ensure consistency in the da... from a large number of companies and used in preparing GMA's submi... National Commission on Food Marketing. For your convenience, the Gu... has been arranged in three sections, corresponding to Schedules A, B ... the enclosed questionnaires:

- SCHEDULE A concerns the sales and marketing activities of your company. It should be completed by the person(s) most familiar with the overall activities of the company as a whole. **ONLY ONE COPY OF SCHEDULE A IS REQUIRED FOR EACH COMPANY.**

- SCHEDULE B deals with distinctly new products introduced by your company, under its own brand names, since January 1, 1954. **ONE COPY OF SCHEDULE B IS TO BE COMPLETED FOR EACH NEW PRODUCT INTRODUCED IN THIS TIME PERIOD.**
  Each copy of Schedule B should be completed by the person(s) most familiar with the particular product concerned. If you have had a significant number of new product introductions, it is possible that several different persons will be involved in com-pletion of the various copies of Schedule B required.

- SCHEDULE C deals with line extensions, product improvements and new product development activities since January 1, 1954. **ONE COPY OF SCHEDULE C IS TO BE COMPLETED FOR EACH PRODUCT CATEGORY IN WHICH ONE OR MORE OF THESE ACTIVITIES HAS OCCURRED.**
  Each copy of Schedule C should be completed by the person(s) most familiar with the product category concerned. As with Sched-ule B, it may thus be necessary for several different persons to be involved in the completion of the various copies of Schedule C required.

An adequate supply of blank questionnaires has been included to permit you to provide the necessary information requested and further, should you wish, to retain copies of the completed questionnaire for your own records. Also, several copies of this Guide are enclosed for possible use by various persons within

Guide - Page 1

CONFIDENTIAL

QUESTIONNAIRE GUIDE

1. <u>Mergers</u>: If, during the time period covered by these questionaires, your company has merged with, or acquired, another company, please respond to questions <u>as though both companies involved were one</u> during the entire time period 1954-64.

2. <u>Estimates</u>: Some of the data requested in these questionnaires <u>may</u> not be available in your records because your company's accounting procedures do not break them out in a separate manner. Such figures, nevertheless, are of great importance to us in examining the changing nature of various expenditures over varying competitive conditions.

Therefore, for any questions listed below for which accounting records do not permit accurate reporting, please instead provide us with <u>estimates</u> of the data in question. In estimating please make every attempt to give an accurate reflection of the time and effort expended by your company on the activity. Do <u>not</u> apply arbitrary methods of allocation (such as percentage-of-sale basis) which fail to meaningfully reflect time and efforts utilized.

The specific questions in which estimates <u>may</u> be necessary are as follows:

> Schedule B -- question 10a
>   questions 10b, columns (5),(6),(7)
>
> Schedule C -- question 2, columns (5)
>   question 4, columns (2),(3)
>   question 5a, columns (4),(5)
>   question 5b, column (5)

Normally, the person(s) best able to prepare such estimates are the line executives most directly concerned. For marketing data, the most qualified are likely to be branch managers, product managers or other line and staff marketing personnel who have been directly involved in the planning or marketing of the product in question. These same persons would also seem to be the best qualified to respond to questions concerning qualitative aspects of the product - for example, Schedule B, question 4. A research and development director may perhaps best estimate research and development allocations for products in question.

3. <u>Time Span</u>: The persons associated with a product introduced several years ago may no longer be with your company or may be unable to recall the events clearly enough to make meaningful estimates. Then, if absolutely necessary, please provide data from January 1, 1961 (in lieu of January, 1954) for the following questions:

Schedule B -- question 4
                question 10a
                question 10b, columns (5),(6),(7) only

Schedule C -- question 3
                question 4, columns (2),(3)
                question 5a, columns (4),(5)

In all other cases except those specifically noted above, however,
please provide data <u>for the full period from January 1, 1954</u>.

SCHEDULE A
COMPANY
INFORMATION

QUESTIONNAIRE GUIDE

Question 1

Please provide data, for the entire period requested, for your company
as a whole. Do not provide data in this section for divisions or other
sub-units of the company unless otherwise requested to do so. If you are
a subsidiary of a larger company, please include data only for your company,
not for the parent company.

Year	Net Domestic Sales of Consumer Food Products	Media Advertising	Sales Force Compensation	Sales Promotion	Marketing Research	Total Research and Development	If total reported in Col. (7) includes basic technological research conducted by or on behalf of your company, please enter check (✓) here.
(1)	(2)	(3)	(4)	(5)	(6)	(7)	(8)
954	x,xxx,xxx	xxx,xxx	xxx,xxx	xx,xxx	xx,xxx	xx,xxx	✓
1955	x,xxx,xxx	xxx,xxx	xxx,xxx	xx,xxx	xx,xxx	xx,xxx	

NOTES

Column (1)

Provide data for calendar year if possible — if not, use your company's
fiscal year and explain its basis in the space provided below.

Column (2)

— Net domestic sales of consumer products only. Do not include
foreign sales, sales to institutional buyers, sales to government
or government agencies.

— Net domestic sales is defined as total revenue (on a delivered price
basis) minus cash discounts and quantity discounts. With regard to
the effect of price deals, please report net domestic sales as you
would in your company's usual accounting practice, but indicate if
the figure shown is:

1. net of all price deals

Guide — Page 5

2. net of some price deals

3. <u>not</u> net of price deals

— Sales figures should be reported <u>net</u> of returns and allowances.
  However, if your accounting practices do not enable you to com-
  pute a net figure, you may provide sales data <u>gross</u> of returns
  and allowances. If you provide gross figures, please so
  indicate in the questionnaire.

Column (3)

— For media advertising, please report <u>only agency billings</u> (or
  its equivalent). It is conceived that such billings would include
  the costs of media space, time and production (art work, plates,
  etc.).

— Agency billings <u>may</u> include expenses other than those associated
  solely with advertising (for example, market research conducted
  by the agency). Differences in company accounting practices,
  however, make it impossible to overcome such a problem entirely.
  Therefore, if your company's accounting practice permits any
  non-advertising costs included in agency billings to be separated
  readily, please subtract such costs from the figure reported. If,
  however, your accounting practice does <u>not</u> permit ready separation
  of such costs, you may report a total figure for all agency billings. If so, please indicate on the schedule those figures which
  include non-advertising costs.

— Do <u>not</u> indicate costs or expenses associated with your company's
  internal advertising department or staff.

— Do <u>not</u> include here the costs of cooperative advertising. Cooperative advertising expenditures should be included in "Sales
  Promotion" (Column (5)).

Column (4)

Sales force compensation includes compensation (salaries, bonuses, com-
missions, sick pay and other benefits) of salesmen, sales supervisors,
managers and sales clerical personnel in the field. It should also
include <u>expenses</u> incurred by these personnel (automobile expenses and
depreciation, travel, etc.).

— Brokerage fees, if incurred, <u>should</u> be included.

— Do <u>not</u> include here salaries of, or expenses incurred for physical
  distribution of the product (e.g. transportation, shipping, warehousing, etc.). Also, do <u>not</u> include costs and expenses of

Guide – Page 6

driver-salesmen.

— If your company sells both through consumer channels <u>and</u> to institutional/government agencies:

   1. If your accounting records enable you to separate figures for sales compensation by type of account, please provide the· expenditure applicable to sales through consumer channels.

   2. If not, but if you have a reasonable basis for allocation of such costs (which is indicative of time and effort involved) such as number of accounts, number of orders, then please allocate on this basis.

   3. If such an allocation is not possible, please allocate on a percentage-of-sale basis.

   4. If it is necessary to allocate in any of the manners specified above, please indicate the method you have used.

Column (5)

— Sales promotion includes couponing, samples, contests, point of purchase material, etc.

— Include sales promotion expenditures both to consumers <u>and</u> to the trade.

— Include here also expenditures on cooperative advertising.

Column (6)

— Includes market analysis, sales analysis, consumer research, advertising research and other similar activities conducted by your company.

   1. Report the total of <u>all</u> such research costs incurred by your company. This should include both internal marketing research costs and expenses <u>and</u> the cost of research conducted on your company's behalf by external agencies or firms.

   NOTE — in reporting test marketing expenditures

   (a) Sales revenue from test marketing should be included in "Net Domestic Sales"(Column 2).

   (b) Advertising, sales force compensation and sales promotion expenses associated with test marketing should be included in Columns (3),(4) and (5) respectively.

Guide - Page 7

(c) Special audits, surveys and other marketing research associated with test marketing should be included in "Marketing Research" (Column (6)).

Column (7)

— Please report the total of <u>all</u> research conducted by your company, by or on its behalf. This includes <u>both</u>:

1. <u>Product research and development</u>, in which funds and effort are expended with the objective of developing or improving a specific product or brand. Such activities might include design, engineering and technical specifications, manufacture of prototypes and other similar activities involving technical development of products.

2. <u>Basic technological research</u>, in which case a company undertakes basic research in a fundamental process or technology. For example, a company might undertake research in the dehydration of food products, or in the chemical structure of vegetable oils. Such research cannot be regarded as relating to a specific product, for no one end product is necessarily visualized at the conception of research activities, and indeed <u>many</u> products may subsequently benefit from this research.

Column (8)

— Place a check (√) in Column (8) if the total in Column (7) <u>includes</u> basic technological research and development.

Question 2

This question asks, in essence, that you provide an "inventory" of new product activity in your company, as that activity relates to the 22 product
categories listed. Please note that the activities described in columns (2),
(3) and (4) of this question are concerned *only* with products marketed, or
intended to be marketed, *under your company's own brand name(s).*
Column (5), however, asks you to indicate those categories in which you have
at some time sold products under wholesalers', retailers' or other distributors'
brands.

In each case, the time period involved is from January 1, 1954 to present.

The following explanatory notes pertain to the columnar headings in the table
used for completion of this question:

Product Categories: The 22 product categories shown are the only ones to be
considered here; the scope of a category should, in each instance, be self-
explanatory. However, if you should be in doubt as to whether one or more
of your company's products belongs in any of these categories, the following
comments may be of assistance:

- The definition of each category that we are employing is that
  utilized by A. C. Nielsen Company in connection with its Retail
  Grocery Index reporting. If your company has access to the
  Nielsen reports, you may resolve your doubts by consulting the
  Nielsen definitions.

- If you do not have access to Nielsen reports, or if you are still
  in doubt, please contact us for clarification.

Distinctly New Products: are regarded as products that are "new" in the sense
that they have been developed wholly or in part by your company, and are substantially different in form, ingredients or processing methods from other products previously marketed by your company. For our purposes here, the fact
a competitor might previously have offered a similar product on the market does
not disqualify your consideration of a product as being distinctly new, providing it otherwise meets the criteria stated above.

As further exemplification of the concept of a "distinctly new product", we
would expect that the introduction of such a product would be characterized by
the concurrent creation of *one or more* of the following:
- Its own separate marketing plan and/or budget.
- Its own separate advertising budget and distinct campaign.

Guide - Page 9

- Its own product manager, if applicable.
- Its own profit and loss statement.
- Its own brand name or product designation.

New *flavors* of existing products, new *package sizes*, and minor *improvements* in existing products are examples of new attributes which are *not* regarded as characteristic of a distinctly new product.

Line Extensions: are new package sizes, flavors or shapes of existing products; they represent *additions* to an existing line of products and as such, employ no fundamental new technology, ingredients or form. A line extension would *not* normally be expected to have its own marketing plan or budget, its own product manager (if applicable), profit and loss statement or distinct brand name; it may, or may not, have its own advertising campaign or budget, but if so, these would normally be employed only at the time of its introduction. Examples of line extensions might be:

- An additional flavor of a line of packaged gelatin desserts.
- A larger-sized box of a cold breakfast cereal to supplement existing smaller sizes of the same cereal.
- A new shape of biscuit, utilizing the same ingredients and processing methods as an existing type.

Product Improvements: are changes in *existing* products, such as changes in ingredients, processing methods, appearance, taste, texture and other changes of a similar order. A change in packaging would also be regarded as a product improvement *if* the change resulted in a package with improved *performance characteristics* (example, longer shelf life), but would not be regarded as an improvement if the packaging change was merely one of color, artistic design or appearance.

Since a product improvement may be regarded as resulting in a "changed product", the form of the product existing prior to the change is presumed to be withdrawn from the market. That is, a product improvement does *not* result in the *addition* of a new product, but rather only in some kind of *amendment* to an existing product. As such, product improvements would *not be* expected to involve new brand names, newly-separate marketing plans or budgets, and so forth. Examples of product improvements might be:

- The use of a new type of oil in a packaged pudding dessert to give better texture to the prepared product.
- The use of a different wrapping material which results in extended shelf life for a cheese product, both in the store and in the home.
- The use of a new processing method in manufacturing cake mixes which results in a product of more uniform quality.

Guide - Page 10

New Product Development: is regarded as any activity carried out by a company which has as its ultimate objective the creation and introduction of a distinctly new product. For purposes of these questionnaires, we further specify that a new product development activity must be one which a company has recognized or designated in some form (e.g., a project number, etc.), and to which specified funds have been allocated and/or expended.

Thus, the following activities might be regarded as new product development activities, *providing* they have been recognized by the company as relating to the development of one or more specific new products:

- Product concept testing.
- Laboratory or kitchen research and development.
- Product testing
- Surveys, questionnaires, interviews and other forms of market research directly relating to one or more specific products or product concepts.

FOR EACH OF THE CHECKS (✓) YOU HAVE MADE IN EACH OF THE PRODUCT CATEGORIES PLEASE NOTE CAREFULLY THE FURTHER ACTION REQUIRED, AS SPECIFIED AT THE BOTTOM OF QUESTION 2.

CONFIDENTIAL   SCHEDULE B
                               DISTINCTLY NEW PRODUCTS
                               INTRODUCED SINCE
                               JANUARY 1, 1954

QUESTIONNAIRE GUIDE

Schedule B should be completed by the person (s) most directly familiar with
the history of the product for which information is given. Please complete
a separate schedule for each distinctly new product introduced since January 1,
1954. Information on line extensions and product improvements should be
given in Schedule C. Complete Schedule B for all products marketed or test
marketed for the first time during the period since January 1, 1954.

Questions 1 - 4   Self-explanatory. Comments as to time span covered apply
to Question 4.

Question 5 This question asks you to indicate the time span elapsed between
the beginning of each basic step in the development of this distinctly new product. Only those steps in the development which would be recognizable in a'
company's budget or schedule as attributable to the development of this specific product are included; hence, such activities as search for new product ideas,
screening of ideas, etc., are not included in this question.

Some of the steps indicated may not have taken place in the development of this
product. If this is the case, write "none" in the blank space opposite the
activity concerned.

The steps for which you are asked to indicate dates, or if these are not known,
time span elapsed, together with explanations of each, are as follows:

STEP	EXPLANATIONS OR ILLUSTRATION
Product Research and Development	Includes research, design, engineering and technical specifications, manufacture of prototypes, feasibility tests and other similar activities involving technical develop-ment of this new product.
Product Testing	Testing of consumer reactions or evaluation of the product, either under experimental condi-tions and/or by in-home use tests.
Test Marketing	
Introduction on Limited Area Basis	A limited area is considered to be some re-gional or sub-regional area which constitutes something less than the company's total mar-keting area.
Full-Scale Introduction Throughout Company's Mar-keting Area	Full-scale introduction is considered as that point at which the product is offered for sale in all (or substantially all) areas to which the company normally distributes its products.

Guide - Page 12

<u>Question 6a</u> This series of questions presents a set of statements which describe attributes which *might* be characteristic of a new product, and ask you to indicate if these attributes are characteristic of this new product.

In each case, the "changes", "improvements", or "reductions" referred to are to be assessed *relative to* products existing in the category prior to introduction of your new product. For example:

- <u>Example 1</u>: If your company introduced a corn oil margarine, and if there already existed four or five other brands of corn oil margarine on the market, you should assess your product relative to existing brands of corn oil margarine.

- <u>Example 2</u>: If you introduced the corn oil margarine at a time when there were no other brands of such a product on the market, then you should assess your product relative to existing brands of ordinary margarine.

- <u>Example 3:</u> If you introduced the *first* dehydrated potato product, then you should assess the product relative to whatever other types of products and/or ingredients might be used by the consumer to prepare a similar dish or meal; for example, fresh potatoes, milk, cheese etc.

Please answer *all* questions "yes", "no", or "not applicable".

<u>Questions 6b, 7, 8, 9</u> Self explanatory.

<u>Question 8</u> If the product in question is so new that your company has been unable to determine its degree of success, please write in "Not Yet Decided."

<u>Question 9</u> Self-explanatory.

Question 10a

Total expenditures on research and development prior to introduction

- The figure reported here should reflect only those
  expenditures on product research and development
  specifically attributable to the development of this
  product. Do not allocate to this product expenditures on basic technological research which were not
  intended solely for this product.

- However, if the development of this product benefitted substantially from other basic technological
  research or product research (on other products)
  conducted by, or on behalf of, your company, please
  so indicate by placing a check ($\checkmark$) beside the
  expenditure figure entered.

- If your company's accounting practice does not permit
  you to provide research and development expenditures
  up to a point coinciding exactly with the date of
  introduction of this product, you may instead provide a total up to the beginning of your company's
  first new accounting period after the introduction
  of the product.

- Comments as to estimates and time period covered
  (see pages 3-4) apply here.

Total expenditures on marketing research prior to introduction

- Please include only those marketing research expenditures directly attributable to this product. Do not
  include the costs of research designed to serve an
  entire product category or group of categories. For
  example, do not include the costs of audit subscrip-
  tions such as the A. C. Nielsen Service, unless such
  services were purchased specifically for this product,
  or of research such as consumer menu studies from which
  a variety of products might benefit.

- Comments as to estimates and time period covered
  (see pages 3-4) apply here.

Question 10b, 10c

QUARTERLY periods for first two years after introduction – Annual thereafter, see instructions above (1)	Total Factory Sales (units) (2)	Total Net Factory Sales ($) (3)	Gross Profit ($) (4)	Marketing Expenditures ($) ($) (5)	Product Research and Development Expenditures ($) (6)	Marketing Research Expenditures ($) (7)	For each period indicate by checking (✓) if distribution was less than throughout company's full marketing area (8)
– – – –	XXX,XXX	XXX,XXX	XXX	XXX	XXX	XXX	✓
– – – –	XXX,XXX	XXX,XXX	XXX	XXX	XXX	XXX	

Column 1

- For the <u>first</u> <u>two</u> <u>years</u> <u>after</u> <u>date</u> <u>of</u> <u>introduction</u>, provide data by quarterly periods. However, if the last quarterly period shown on this basis is <u>not</u> the final quarter in your company's fiscal year, please provide additional data up to the beginning of the next full fiscal year.

- For periods <u>after</u> the final period shown on the above basis, and up to the present, provide data on an <u>annual</u> basis only.

- If your company's records indicating quarterly data are no longer accessible, then please provide annual data for the entire time span covered.

Column 2

- Factory sales units may be pounds, standard cases, or whatever other unit you usually use. Be sure to indicate the nature of the units you quote.

Column 3

- Total net factory sales is defined as total revenue (on a delivered price basis) <u>minus</u> cash discounts, quantity discounts, and returns and allowances.

  1. <u>Treatment of price deals</u>: When reporting Total Net Factory Sales, the effect of price deals should be indicated.

Guide - Page 15

That is, report Total Net Factory Sales as you would in your company's usual accounting practice, but please indicate if the figure shown is:

    a. Net of all price deals, or

    b. Net of some price deals, or

    c. Not net of price deals.

2. If your company's accounting practices force you to provide a figure <u>gross</u> of returns and allowances, please so indicate on the Schedule.

Column 4

- Gross Profit is defined as Total Net Factory Sales <u>minus</u> Direct Cost of Goods Sold where:

  <u>Direct Cost of Goods Sold</u> is treated as including <u>only</u> <u>direct manufacturing costs</u>: raw materials, packaging materials, direct labor, supplies, and other manufacturing costs directly associated with the manufacture of the product. Cost of goods sold should <u>not</u> include allocated overhead expenses.

Column 5

- This total should include <u>only</u>:

  1. Media advertising   )
) as defined in Schedule A,
  2. Sales force compensation)
)
  3. Sales promotion   ) question 1 of this Guide

- Comments as to estimates and time period covered (see pages 3-4) apply here.

Column 6

- The comments for question 10a also apply here; that is, include only those expenditures on <u>product</u> research and development directly attributable to this product.

- If, in question 10a, you have provided data up to the start of a convenient accounting period (rather than to the exact date of introduction), please ensure that research

expenditures given in question 10b start at the point where
those of question 10a leave off. That is, do not double-
count any expenditure data or leave gaps between periods.

- Comments as to estimates and time period covered (see
pages 3-4) apply here.

Column 7

- As in question 10a, provide data only for those marketing
research expenditures directly attributable to this product. Avoid double-counting of any expenditures shown in
10a.

- Comments as to estimates and time period covered (see
pages 3-4) apply here.

Column 8

- A check mark should be made if distribution of this product
is not throughout your company's full domestic marketing
area.

CONFIDENTIAL   **SCHEDULE C**

                          **LINE EXTENSIONS, PRODUCT
                          IMPROVEMENTS AND NEW
                          PRODUCT DEVELOPMENT,
                          SINCE JANUARY 1, 1954**

QUESTIONNAIRE GUIDE

Please complete one copy of this schedule for *each product category* in
which you have:

1. Introduced line extensions since January 1, 1954, regardless
   of the date of introduction of the original product,

   and/or

2. Made product improvements since January 1, 1954, regardless
   of the date of introduction of the original product,

   and/or

3. Engaged in some new product development work during part or
   all of the period since January 1, 1954 which did not result
   or has not yet resulted, in distinctly new products being introduced to the market.

<u>Question 1</u>   Self-explanatory

Question 2   For definition and examples of <u>line</u> <u>extensions</u> refer to the
Guide for Schedule A, Question 2.

Year (1)	Number of line extensions introduced. (2)	Number of previous extensions withdrawn (3)	Total Sales Volume (Net Factory Sales) of all products in this category marketed by your company (dollars) (4)	Percentage (on dollar basis) of your total category sales accounted for by line extensions introduced since Jan. 1, 1954 (5)
1954	X X	X X	XXX,XXX	X X
1955	X X	X X	XXX,XXX	X X

<u>Column (1)</u>

- Provide data for calendar year if possible. If not, use your company's fiscal year and explain its basis in the space provided below.

<u>Columns (2) and (3)</u>

- Line extensions, as defined in the context of this questionnaire, are new package sizes, flavors, or shapes of existing products. In addressing the question of the <u>number</u> of line extensions, we provide this guide line as to what should be regarded as a "unit" of line extension.

1. A new flavor of an existing product would be regarded as <u>one</u> line extension. Since the basic extension activity here is the new flavor itself, this would be considered as one extension <u>only</u> even if the new flavor was packaged in three or four different sizes in which the "parent" product was also packaged at the time of introduction of the new flavor.

2. Similarly, a new package size would be <u>one</u> extension even if the package was introduced in all existing flavors of the product in question. Once again, the focus of attention should be upon the nature of the extension activity involved.

Guide - Page 19

Column (4)

- Total Net Factory Sales. For full explanation of this figure, refer to Questionnaire Guide, Schedule B, Question 10.

Column (5)

- This percentage should be computed on a basis of sales <u>dollar</u> volume, rather than on a basis of <u>unit</u> volume. The use of a sales dollar volume base has been selected in order to conform to the format of data requested in Column (4).

<u>Question 3</u>   For definition and examples of <u>product improvements</u> refer to the Guide for Schedule A, Question 2.

This question asks you to provide a brief chronology of product improvements made by your company during the period since January 1, 1954. The description of improvements need not be a lengthy one; a brief statement indicating the physical nature of the improvement, and the purpose it serves, is sufficient. Examples of adequate descriptions would be:

- Use of a new vegetable oil ingredient to improve texture of the product when prepared by housewife.

- Utilization of an improved processing method for pre-sifting ingredients to avoid excessive lumping.

- New Polyethylene packaging material to extend shelf life by 50% over existing packaging material.

Please complete Question 3 for <u>each product</u> in the category.

Please list only <u>significant</u> product improvements. As a guideline here, we would regard a significant improvement to be one in which distinct communication or mention of the improvement was made in the product's advertising sales promotion, label, or presentations by salesmen.

Comments as to time span covered (see page 3b) apply here.

<u>Question 4</u>

Column (2)

- Please include <u>only</u> those research expenditures directly attributable to line extensions and product improvement. Do <u>not</u> include basic technological research or research in other product categories from which <u>this</u> product may have benefitted.

Guide – Page 20

- Comments as to estimates and time span covered apply here.

<u>Column (3)</u>

- Report <u>only</u> those marketing research expenditures directly attributable to line extensions or product improvements in this category.

- The cost of any test marketing conducted should <u>only</u> reflect the costs of surveys, audits or other special research associated with the test market. Please do <u>not</u> include advertising, selling and other associated expenses here.

- Comments as to estimates and time span covered apply here.

<u>Question 5a</u>. For definition and examples of <u>product</u> development, refer to Guide for Schedule A, Question 2.

Please note that this question deals <u>only</u> with the development of distinctly new products. In this context, the term "product" is used to refer to any concept, idea or proposal that is recognized in your company's budgets or schedules as a separate entity.

Question 5a deals <u>only</u> with product development activities which have been <u>terminated</u>, and for which a product was <u>not</u> introduced to the marketplace. Question 4b to follow deals with product development activities <u>currently</u> being undertaken.

Please complete the table, as requested, concerning development of distinctly new products <u>not</u> introduced.

Year (1)	Number of distinctly new products for which funds were expended on development, but for which further development was terminated, after:		Expenditures on development of distinctly new products, which were not introduced to the marketplace, on:	
	Product research & development (No. of products) (2)	Product testing (No. of products) (3)	Product Research & Development (Dollars) (4)	Marketing Research (Dollars) (5)
1954	X X	X X	XX,XXX	XX,XXX
1955	X X	X X	XX,XXX	XX,XXX

Guide - Page 21

Column (2)

- Product research and development includes research, design, engineering and technical specifications, manufacture of prototypes, feasibility tests and other similar activities involving technical development of new products.

Column (3)

- Product testing refers to the testing of <u>consumer</u> reactions to the product, either under experimental conditions and/or by in-home use tests.

Columns (4) and (5)

- Concepts of product research and development, and marketing research, used previously in this Schedule apply here.

- Comments on estimates and time span covered (see pages 3-4) apply here.

<u>Question 5b.</u> Self-explanatory. Concepts of <u>Product Research and Development</u> and of <u>Marketing Research</u> used previously in this Schedule apply. Please note that Question 5b deals only with new products <u>currently</u> under development.

Comments as to estimates (see pages 3-4) apply here.

Index